Renaissance Jewels and Jeweled Objects

Frontispiece: The necklace is catalogue number 59; the ship pendant is number 49.

RENAISSANCE JEWELS AND JEWELED OBJECTS

FROM

THE MELVIN GUTMAN COLLECTION

Introduction and Catalogue by Parker Lesley

THE BALTIMORE MUSEUM OF ART

1968

Copyright © 1968 The Baltimore Museum of Art
Wyman Park, Baltimore, Maryland 21218

Library of Congress Catalogue Card No. 67–17585

Preface

Melvin Gutman is not inclined to discuss his claims to fame, but he does love to dwell upon his past history as an athlete, and it is not too difficult to get him to talk about the history of his collecting, which he does with wit, and not a little whimsy.

He is the most recent of a series of four "M's" in the Gutman family, for his father, his grandfather and his great-grandfather were respectively Malvin, Moses and Manuel Gutman. The last named, who arrived in the United States and settled in Baltimore during the Federal Period, has been called "a tyrannical lover of life who had an affection for good living, fine brandy and cigars." He established a key for the life of the family, the echoes of which are discernible today.

The Baltimore connection of the three Gutmans has been pursued through the Baltimore Directory. Manuel Gutman's name is not listed; Moses Gutman's appears first in the Directory of 1853 as a clothier at 155 West Pratt Street. Two years later Moses Gutman and Company, Clothiers, were known at 331 West Baltimore Street, but Moses was still dwelling at the West Pratt Street address. His name continues in the Directories until 1869, about which time he moved from Baltimore to Wheeling, West Virginia, and established himself, with his son Malvin, in the manufacture and sale of clothing.

During the course of a purchasing trip to New York City Malvin met and married a member of the Newborg family, which had been prominent in securities trading there for many years. Malvin Gutman became known as an astute trader on Wall Street, but likewise for his many philanthropies, among them the support of one of the oldest and best established homes for the aged in New York at that time. Indeed, this home was under his personal direction after he retired from active business at the age of forty and until the time of his death.

He collected antiquities; he also had an interest in books and formed a very extensive library of rare volumes on travel. These preoccupations, and his frequent travel abroad with his family, established a way of life and thought for his son, Melvin.

He had wanted his son to go into law as a profession. In point of fact, Melvin made a valiant effort and spent several years studying to be an attorney.

Having met all of the prerequisites to a legal career, and on the threshold of final commitment by examination for the bar, Melvin Gutman found that his interests in art, athletics and a strong desire to enjoy the pleasures of a classical *Wanderung* were not to be denied, and he set forth to prove his mettle independently. He first established himself on an international basis as a leading tennis and hockey player; a frequent doubles partner was the son of the former Kaiser, Wilhelm II, as well as other notables in the international tennis set. Moreover, he was at one time a member of the "Saint Nicks," the prominent New York hockey team, then a major amateur club.

By virtue of his education and background, Melvin Gutman was in an excellent position to take full advantage of the remarkable opportunities afforded him to study European art at the fountainhead, in the museums and cathedrals of the old world. Moreover, he had access to private collections and it would appear that this European experience later stood him in good stead. Returning to New York and to business, he was affiliated principally with the house of Newborg from 1918 to 1927. He had the good sense—as has been observed ruefully by others—to get out of the market at the proper moment prior to the debacle of 1929. What seems important here is that his business astuteness generated the funds and developed the acumen necessary to the acquisition of one of the best collections of antique jewelry.

An aesthete among Pharisees, his attention was first captured by Persian miniatures and subsequently by Oriental porcelains. With emphasis upon works of quality and with a preference for pure calligraphy in the work of important Persian miniaturists, he gathered a collection featuring several important complete manuscripts. This has since been disbursed through gifts to museums in the United States. Similarly, he has now disposed of his collection of porcelains of the Ming and earlier Chinese dynasties.

Since settling in New York, Melvin Gutman has become a true Manhattanite and has not left the city or its environs since 1927. The shattering influence of World War II, and the resultant disbursal of European family collections as well as the influx of large numbers of European refugees into the United States provided an unparalleled opportunity for Melvin Gutman to deal in, to study and to acquire for his own collection, works which had hitherto not been accessible. Over many years he owned and managed the Cole Galleries on Third Avenue, a crossroads for the exchange of ancient jewelry and the most intriguing shop of its kind I ever knew. Through the years he has acquired a substantial reputation in art circles of New York and has been regularly turned to for guidance on matters relating to antique jewelry. Indeed, he has been called upon on numerous occasions by foremost museums of this country, and the Departments of State and Treasury, to assist with the innumerable knotty problems which arise out of a confused and complex field of art and scholarship. I, myself, first met Melvin Gutman at the Cole Galleries in this connection when I turned to him for advice regarding an exhibition of Renaissance jewelry at Oberlin College in 1959.

Collecting jewelry should be more than a mere gathering of objects and result in more than ownership of pieces which have had a long previous history of distinguished ownership, for such histories, valuable as they are, are only indirectly related to the question of the quality of the collection and of jewels as works of art. A higher order of understanding is required for the collector who seeks to build a truly magnificent collection for himself, electing to act upon his own knowledge and instinct. We may surmise that the ability to make quick and sound decisions such as that which characterizes a good businessman who has learned to weigh risk and reward, served Melvin Gutman well. He learned to temper desire with knowledge, and his experience with instinct. Not infrequently, on the threshold of discovery, he had to trust his instinct and make a decision in the absence of verifiable scholarly information.

Melvin Gutman surrounded himself with a fine library, including catalogues of major collections and other reference material, photographs, reproductions, sales catalogues and books on jewelry, much of it of great value in its own right. Assiduous study of these documents and a first-hand knowledge of the contents of fine old collections have made it possible for him to recognize and acquire several major examples of jewelry, the attributions and ownership of which had since been forgotten by others. To this bookish advantage he added an extensive knowledge of the techniques of the goldsmith and the lapidary, and a photographic recall of details and descriptions. I must thank Mr. Gutman at this point for the loan of relevant parts of this extensive library and documentation, without which this present volume could not have been produced with as much facility.

6

Melvin Gutman has been most obliging in the loan of his collections; he has exhibited them at the Art Institute of Chicago (1951–1962), has lent generously to the Detroit Institute of Arts, and for several years has had on indefinite loan at the Allen Art Museum, Oberlin College, 180 pieces from his spendid collection of Ancient and Medieval gold, which was catalogued in detail and fully illustrated in their *Bulletin* in 1961. He has also made donations to the Norfolk Museum of Arts and Sciences.

Mr. Gutman has often said to me that he wants his possessions to be available for study and appreciation by the widest interested audience, and he has been characteristically generous in placing over 250 Renaissance jewels and jeweled objects on loan at The Baltimore Museum of Art since 1962. This present volume catalogues 70 significant pieces out of this number, and the rest will follow in a second volume. These 70 were chosen not only because of the great intrinsic merit, but also because of the intriguing fascination of the challenge that they offer to the serious researcher. The ensuing volume will include, *inter alia*, his fine collections of medals and medallions, an extraordinary selection of fine rings and portrait miniatures in their original cases.

For myself, I can say that the pleasure of knowing Melvin Gutman has been one of the delights of my life. He claims to be cantankerous and difficult, but I have always found him witty, honest, frank and engagingly playful. It is always a pleasure to call on him and such a call is invariably filled with profitable and interesting conversation.

Professor Parker Lesley, an old acquaintance of both Mr. Gutman and myself, and whose introductory essay and catalogue follows, has surmounted a most difficult task; readers will not fail to perceive the difficulty that any research in this field encounters. But in the end the sheer pleasure of working with such objects and the delights of discovery have far outweighed the frustrations of painstaking research.

As this book goes to press we have received the sad news of the death of Melvin Gutman. There is no question that this document of his interests and connoisseurship now becomes a memorial to a man whose collecting and whose personal interests are reflected in the generosity of his loans to this and other museums. We regret that he did not live to see this publication.

CHARLES PARKHURST, *Director*
The Baltimore Museum of Art

Acknowledgments

This catalogue was begun with the anticipation that it would be completed in twelve months. That was four years ago. The work was protracted, and at times suspended, by many factors: differences of conviction that had to be arbitrated, last-minute intelligence which meant the revision of entire passages, illness, and the accumulation of some knowledge which, as it grew, made all the more arresting my insufficiency for the business in hand. Throughout the reversals and fretfulness, the qualms and infrequent certainties, I have been sustained, encouraged and, on occasion, chastened by the aid of all those whose names are mentioned below. Their aid, indeed, has been so copious that the by-line is an extravagance. This volume is a collaboration. To my collaborators, for their help as described, these thanks are due:

To Melvin Gutman who has been, in the end, the "onlie begetter" of the undertaking. With a patience as great as his unselfishness, and a fortitude in the face of controversy and my inexperience that is beyond praise or gratitude, he is in truth the *auctor*, the producer, of these pages.

To Charles Parkhurst, Director of The Baltimore Museum of Art, who is responsible for so much reclamation and repair within the manuscript, and so much understanding and reassurance, that only his own scruples prevent his name from appearing as co-author.

Before me at all times have remained the example and recollections of Joan Evans, D. Litt., F.S.A., whose hospitality, wisdom and genial wit are equaled only by the generosity with which she put her learning at the disposal of an inquisitive novice.

To Dr. Gertrude Rosenthal, for searching suggestions on matters of style; to Mrs. Romaine Stec Somerville, who transcribed the descriptions of the pieces and whose fine eye was responsible for many improvements; to Victor Covey, who analyzed materials and detected restorations; to Hiram Woodward, who compiled and cross-referenced the initial bibliography and scutinized references; to Mrs. Frances Rome, who undertook the exhausting task of measuring the pieces; to several other members of the museum staff, especially Mrs. Beatrice Chambliss, for initial and frequent aid; to Mrs. Diana Johnson, for periodic research; to Mrs. Barbara Fuchsman, for much library assistance and to William Hommel who, as Registrar, provided access to the originals when they had to be studied *in manu*.

To Dr. Sergius Yakobson, Dr. Elemer Bako, Dr. Edgar Breitenbach and Dr. Alan Fern of The Library of Congress, for formidable and forbearing labors on problems of translation, iconography and bibliography; to Dr. Cornelius Vermeule, of the Museum of Fine Arts, Boston, and to Prof. Eric Sjöqvist and Dr. Frances F. Jones, both of Princeton University, for advice on style and iconography; to Dr. Yvonne Hackenbroch of The Metropolitan Museum of Art, for many suggestions as to parallels and similar pieces; to Miss Dorothy Miner, Miss Dorothy Kent Hill and Richard H. Randall of the Walters Art Gallery, Baltimore, for bibliographical assistance and connoisseurship.

To Hugh Tait, F.S.A., Assistant Keeper of the Department of British and Medieval Antiquities of the British Museum, for opinions on various pieces and for making accessible to me the accession books of the Waddesdon Bequest; to C. C. Oman, retired Keeper of the Department of Metalwork of the Victoria and Albert Museum, for diagnoses of most of the objects in the collection and for putting at my disposal museum records; to Prof. Dr. Erich Steingräber of the Germanisches Nationalmuseum, Nürnberg, for the elucidation of technical and iconographical points; to Dr. Klemens Stadler, Director of the Bavarian State Archives, for heraldic information; to Dr. Ernst Brochhagen of the Stiftung Preussischer Kulturbesitz, Staatliche Museen, Gemäldegalerie, Berlin, for information on Alexander Cooper; and to C. R. Humphery-Smith, Director of the Institute of Heraldic and Genealogical Studies, Canterbury, for heraldic and dialectal enlightenment.

My indebtedness to the following goes far beyond specification: to the Old Dominion Educational Foundation, to Dean E. Vernon Peele and my colleagues in the Department of Art at Old Dominion College, for financial and academic support throughout leaves-of-absence and erratic truancies.

There have been many others who have made recommendations, voiced reservations and offered critiques. To these past, present and future I submit the words of Ben Jonson:

> We have set down that that in our judgment agreeth best with reason and good order. Which notwithstanding, if it seem to any to be too rough hewed, let him plane it out more smoothly, and I shall not only not envy it, but in the behalf of my country most heartily thank him for so great a benefit; hoping that I shall be thought sufficiently to have done my part if in tolling this bell I may draw others to a deeper consideration of the matter; for, touching myself, I must needs confess that after much painful churning this only would come which here we have devised."

PARKER LESLEY

Table of Contents

Introduction

To the Various Readers

This excursion into the domain of jewelry has different ends and different routes by which each end is to be reached. To the collector belongs the catalogue proper and its evaluation of the pieces on critical grounds. To the museum belongs also the catalogue proper, with its data and physical descriptions, which are minute out of conviction that the combination of photographs and textual particulars makes for a permanent account. The discussion of the pieces appertains to the scholar. Here alternatives are posed and comparisons are offered. For the doctrinaire many may not be exhaustive; it is hoped that for the wise they are relevant enough. To the public is directed this Introduction, the purpose of which is "to lead into" what has been gathered together as a good guide leads a visitor about a monument: he quickens perception, but does not overrule sight. The casually curious may sample here and there. The cataloguer's is, of course, the whole, with whatever defects or virtues the whole possesses. In perhaps realized lucid balance, in tempered excitement and persuadable scepticism, in the stubborn craving for sense and significance lie the rewards of any inventive reshaping of materialized ideas. The whole is the cataloguer's creation. The word is used willfully, for if creation—process beyond making—is within human powers at all, in what does it lie if not in merging materials and thoughts into an intelligible order?

On Purposes and Definitions

This volume is the first of two which will constitute in effect a *catalogue raisonné* of the Melvin Gutman Collection and it is therefore relevant to devote a few words to what a catalogue of this sort is and should be. Granted that the purpose of a catalogue is neither to sell nor to stupefy, what is it? Here terms must be defined.

In the popular mind the word "catalogue" denotes two kinds of compilation. One is commercial and may vary from the highly technical listing of automobile parts to the frankly enticing, often coercive belles-lettres of the book publisher or the horticulturist. The function of these essays is to convince that the objects purchased will benefit the reader in wonder-working ways. No little legislation touches on the gentle control of abuses. The other catalogue is the scholarly species from which, on the whole, the public is excluded. Its function is to perpetuate verbally and pictorially a given grouping of objects and to exhaust, insofar as time and endurance permit, the questions the objects propound. Because the scholarly audience is professional and limited, with rituals and observances of its own, a catalogue produced according to their standards may be just as open to abuses as its commercial counterpart. These, rather than resting upon hyperbole, will arise from over-scrupulousness and exaggerated formalism, a morbid fear of omissions, incompletion or any relaxation into levity. The objects, instead of being lighted up, are shadowed by pedantry and sealed off from understanding by an impermeable crust of erudition. No legislation has ever brought this propensity under control.

In order to be neat and explicit, it is preferable to return to etymologies, to use word sources as the stones on which constructions lie. *Catalogue* derives from the Late Latin *catalogus*, from the Greek καταλόγος, "a counting up, list," from καταλεγείν, "to count up" (κατά, "down, completely" + λεγείν, "to pick out, gather, count, say"). Thus, strictly, a catalogue is no more than a list, a counting or summing up.

Collection derives from the Old French *collecter*, from the Latin *collecta*, "a gathering" and *collectus*, past participle of *colligere*, "to bind together" (*col* + *legere*, "to gather"). Thus further, the catalogue of a collection is "a summing up of what has been gathered."

Jewelry derives from the Old French *juel* and *juelerie*, from the Late Latin *jocalis*, "pertaining to play," from *jocus*, "play, jest, a joke." Thus finally, the catalogue of a collection of jewelry could be no more than "a summing up of playthings gathered."

But such would be trivial and beggared of meaning. Etymologies should point toward our destination, which must be broadened by paraphrase. A summing up results in a total; a total is a unity to be pondered aside from its parts. A collection is also that which is bound together: by a period of time, a medium, a theme or an intention. What is gathered here is bound together by the fact of being jewelry: objects of delight which, through the richness of their colors, the opulence of their materials and the felicity of their craft deserve deference and imagination. Thus the word-sources are not falsified by defining a catalogue of a collection of jewelry as a volume containing what can be said about the objects of delight which have been bound together by the collector.

"What can be said" . . . to whom? To everyone who has given to, or may use, this publication: the collector, the museum and all its personnel, the public, scholars and the curious at near and far remove. Each has privileges and expectations. The collector must become increasingly informed of the worth of what he has gathered: merits should be praised without adulation and faults assessed without contempt. The museum should have an exact and proficient record of the pieces, so that its custodianship is centralized and disencumbered. The discerning public—to which this catalogue is most especially addressed—should be further informed, gratified and stimulated, with its every reasonable question anticipated and answered, or, at least, signalized. Scholars should be satisfied that the information is precise, that opinions advanced are not mere caprices, and that the examination, both physical and intellectual, of every object has been faithful and thorough. And the curious, the insistent challengers, those troublesome askers of "Why?" should be forestalled and appeased.

All this must somehow be achieved without excess, in proportion, with fitness and equilibrium by the cataloguer, who is part designer, part diviner and part drudge. For him to undertake so sensitive and (always potentially to someone) disaffecting a task requires a goal beyond the desires to please, to memorialize, to judge, to search out or to explain. This is the paradoxical goal of the art historian, that "recorder of things made," to be creative with the creations of others. Upon these products of bygone skills, with their almost uninterpretable freight of vanished and altered meaning, he must impose a meaning of his own that will sustain him and, at the completion of his labor, give forth a comfort and an elation no less mysterious and authoritative than theirs.

Jewelry and Art Historical Inquiry

Jewelry, as a territory to be pacified along art-historical lines, could hardly be more hostile. The obstacles to certainty, the interference of chance and unknown events, the anonymity of craftsmen, the absence of assembled pictorial data—all the restraints upon method and knowledge are so effective that only in rare instances can an assertion be made without some provision for doubt. A summary of the problem might be instructive even though the summary could be interpreted as the cataloguer's expedient *apologia pro operibus suis*.

The art historian who studies a painting, a building or a work of sculpture has before him an object which, more often than not, can be related to a maker, an episode, an environment or other set of human experiences. The anonymous picture may have an identifiable sitter, a period costume or subject matter which can be synchronized with other monuments. Seldom is a building so mean or so vacant of history as to be unconnected with a documented personage. Figurative sculpture, even if extracted from its context, can be settled again within a kindred group. It is the art historian's method to select a body of salient knowns and arrange examples around these in ranks of diminishing explicitness until only the indeterminate remain. The student proceeds, in time-sequence and culture pattern, from the known and explicable to the less known and explicable by firmly placed stepping stones: from a master to "pupil of," to "school of," to "circle of," to "follower of," to "in the manner of," to "unknown."

Since most students of the history of jewelry are also art historians, this method is both habitual and prescribed. But the material is not susceptible to a disposal so trim and systematic. First, the number of pieces decisively the work of an identified craftsman is very sparse: of the 186 examples illustrated by Dr. Joan Evans in *A History of Jewellery, 1100–1870*, only eleven bear the names of makers.

Second, the rapacity of nature and humankind has pillaged our stock of jewelry of all but a fraction. A glance at the inventories of Marie de Medici (Bruel, 1908), of Jean, Duke of Berry (Guiffrey, 1894), of King Charles V of France (Labarte, 1879), of Jeanne d'Evreux (Montaiglon, 1861), is enough to show that even so rich a collection as that of the Munich Schatzkammer is no more than a nostalgic sample.

Third, jewels are seldom in their original condition: stones have been replaced, sections added and subtracted, enamels refilled, frames substituted, chains and fastenings attached, and settings modified to comply with the demands of fashion, fortune or felony. Even such noble examples as the Canning Jewel in the British Museum and the Widener Morse in the National Gallery of Art are not without their probable alterations.

Fourth, the craftsmen were migrant as birds: in 1496, 112 master goldsmiths of foreign origin were recorded by the Goldsmith's Company as working in London (Herbert, 1836, II, p. 121). It would have been not at all remarkable for a young man to have learned his craft in Milan, followed Bona Sforza with her retinue to Cracow in 1518, proceeded to Nürnberg or Augsburg after her departure in 1548, worked for Cosimo I de Medici (1519–1574) in Florence, and died in Valladolid before 1560 as a court jeweler to Philip II.

Fifth, the interaction of designs produced by graphic artists in one part of Europe and adapted by goldsmiths in other parts often makes the relevancy of a design and its offspring only a pleasant speculation.

Sixth, the craftsmen as "minor" rather than "major" artists were impregnated by a communal, still medieval workshop tradition in which common usage prevailed over individual techniques or distinctive mannerisms: the "handwritings" we use to separate one painter from another are not apparent in the jewelers' conformity to practice.

15

And seventh, the jewel as an ornament, as an abstract structure often without imagery, is frequently wanting in those allusions to human activity which offer testimony to a time, a place or a temperament.

The field, then, is embarrassed by anonymity, by scarcity, by alteration, by instability, by dispersion, by conventionalism and by its aniconic character. Most of the routines by which the art historian establishes his conclusions disintegrate. To assemble similar pieces around a dated prototype is hazardous, because not only are there too few such prototypes but the secondary example may also have been fabricated elsewhere. To form groups around the prints of a particular designer is ineffectual, for the designs were internationally disseminated and may, indeed, have been engraved *after* the fashion they were supposed to have set was stabilized: art historical ideology alone is responsible for the assumption that a jewel must necessarily follow chronologically a kindred design. To search for special technical idiosyncrasies, and use these to support the identity of a "school" or "workshop" is likewise defeasible, in view of the craftsmen's notorious mobility.

As if all this were not handicap enough, the art historian's professional system, which is legalistic and arrives at verdicts through precedent, is in the case of jewelry an erring and delusive system. Whereas with painting, architecture, sculpture and some areas of the decorative arts (e.g., ceramics) the bibliography is enormous and enough opinions may be reviewed to tally a fair pronouncement, the history and connoisseurship of jewelry are limited and beset by foibles.

The major volumes on jewelry (apart from articles in learned periodicals and monographs on restricted topics) began over a century ago with Lacroix and Seré's *Histoire de l'orfèvrerie-joaillerie . . .* of 1850. This was followed by Barbet de Jouy's *Les gemmes et joyaux de la Couronne*, 1865; two volumes by Castellani, *Antique Jewellery and its Revival*, 1862, and *Della Orifeceria Italiana*, 1872; Davillier's *Recherches sur l'orfèvrerie en Espagne au moyen âge et à la Renaissance*, 1879; Fontenay's *Les bijoux anciens et modernes*, 1881; Luthmer's *Goldschmuck der Renaissance*, 1881 and *Der Schatz des Freiherrn Karl von Rothschild*, 1883; Molinier's *Dictionnaire des Émailleurs . . .*, 1885; Bapst's *Histoire des Joyaux de la Couronne de France*, 1889, and *Du rôle économique des joyaux dans la vie politique . . .*, 1887; Hefner-Alteneck's *Deutsche Goldschmiedewerke des sechzehnten Jahrhunderts*, 1890; and Havard's *Histoire de l'orfèvrerie française*, 1896. To the beginning of the 20th century the founders of the study were preponderantly French, and their works, though now in the main supplanted, reflect that alliance of elegance, proficiency and casualness which is the charm and failing of French scholarship. For the next half-century the hegemony was German. Rücklin's *Das Schmuckbuch* appeared in 1901; Barth's *Das Geschmeide, Schmuck- und Edelsteinkunde* in 1903; Forrer's *Geschichte des Gold- und Silberschmuckes . . .* in 1905; Haberlandt's *Völkerschmuck* in 1906, Smith's *Jewellery* in 1908; Bassermann-Jordan's *Der Schmuck* in 1909; Williamson's *Catalogue* of the Morgan jewels in 1910; Rosenberg's *Studien über Goldschmiedekunst in der Sammlung Figdor* in 1911; Dalton's *Catalogue* of the Franks Bequest in 1912; von Falke's catalogues of the Eugen Gutman Collection in 1912 and the Kunsthaus, Zurich in 1928; Kunz's *Rings* in 1917; Rosenberg's *Geschichte der Goldschmiedekunst auf technischer Grundlage*, 1918–1924; Joan Evans' *English Jewellery* in 1921; Sponsel's *Das Grüne Gewölbe*, 1925–1932; Bunt's *The Goldsmiths of Italy . . .* in 1926; Kris' *Meister und Meisterwerke der Steinschneidekunst . . .* in 1929; Oman's *Catalogue of Rings*, Victoria and Albert Museum, in 1930; the guide to the Munich Schatzkammer in 1931; Johnson's *Hispanic Silverwork* in 1944 and Kurtesz' *Historia Universal de las Joyas* in 1947. No one can disparage the learning, the exhaustiveness or even the tedium of the German contributions.

16

In 1953 the first truly deep examination of the subject, Joan Evans' *A History of Jewellery, 1100–1870*, was published. This work, the distillation of more than 35 years of study, with its clarity of presentation, its nicety of choice and diagnosis, and its bountiful documentation and literary references, places every subsequent scholar irredeemably in her debt. In the same year Bradford's *Four Centuries of European Jewellery* appeared: it is a less complete but eminently useful work. Steingräber's *Alter Schmuck* is becomingly illustrated and has a compact and instructive text (English translation, *Antique Jewellery*, 1957). Most recently Gans' *Juwelen en mensen*, 1961, has begun the systematic comparison of extant jewels with those in dated portraits (mainly Dutch), a method of establishing date and provenance not altogether indisputable but so far insufficiently employed. Biehn's *Juwelen und Preziosen*, 1965, is handy and competent. Hugh Tait of the British Museum is currently the most careful and constructive of the younger savants, and it is to be hoped that his articles will eventually lead to a general study of equal excellence.

The Melvin Gutman Collection itself has been the subject of M. L. D'Otrange's "A Collection of Renaissance Jewels at the Art Institute of Chicago" in *Connoisseur*, September 1952, an article distinguished for its illustrations. Many objects have been used by Hackenbroch (listed in the Bibliography) as illustrations for her speculations.

In most of the standard works above-mentioned a comprehensible but misapplied national bias or patriotic prejudice is to be observed. Most especially the Germans are prone to make *deutsch* whatever is homeless and particularly fine. The tendency is no more mischievous than any competitive sport, though, as in competitive sport, the winner is not of necessity wise.

Finally, the student of jewelry is dependent on the sales catalogue and the catalogue of exhibitions. The former must be used with maximum wariness, even though (as in the great German sales) the text is often the disinterested performance of notable authority. A vendor puts the best possible face on his wares: if the face is rejuvenated beyond recognition, there are always the escape-clauses of the "conditions of sale." Sale catalogues have their preferences also. For some reason—perhaps because of the long ascendancy of Italian Renaissance studies—North Italian origins seem to be fancied. The frailty of exhibition catalogues lies in etiquette: the lender's attribution remains unquestioned. In any event, the preparation of a loan exhibition scarcely permits time to be allotted for extensive critical research. In both sales and exhibition catalogues, repetition—uncritical, expedient or enforced—may lead to acceptance and then to veneration. Once an object has reached the sanctuary of hard covers it is exceedingly awkward to dislodge.

With such a state of affairs obtaining, how is the cataloguer to proceed, without opening himself, at one point or another, to charges of timidity, credulity or *lèse-majesté*?

This Cataloguer's Method

"Man has always sought to understand himself and his universe by the simple mechanics of sorting," wrote Robert Lindner.

Division into categories was the first venture. The cataloguer had before him the choice of different systems: objects could have been grouped according to chronology, geography, material, iconography or morphography. For reasons plain from the foregoing paragraphs, no one of these was reliable. Applied singly, each ended with a welfare worker's nightmare of miscegenation and gypsy orphans. The arrangement at last adopted here is a composite of all five, the sequence proceeding from a personal and associative logic which, in turn, developed out of numerous sortings and re-sortings.

The first categories established were two: objects worn on the person and objects not so worn, or articles of costume and articles independent of costume. These were classified then generally according to type. Within each type-grouping the objects were then arranged according to previously established data by country and date. In this present Volume I are catalogued crosses, pendants, necklaces and bracelets, lockets, pharmacies and pomanders and certain miscellaneous pieces; in the subsequent Volume II, soon to be published, will be pendants with animals and birds, rings, girdles and belts, framed miniatures, watches, badges and pins, medals, plaques, *coupes*, beakers and flasks, eating utensils and some miscellaneous items of great interest.

At this point physical examination and description was undertaken. Each piece was measured in inches and centimeters. It was then subjected to minute examination under a low-power, binocular microscope of 40 power magnification manufactured by the Spencer American Optic Company. Whenever practicable pieces were dismantled and reassembled. Microscopic and ocular impressions were consolidated into a description of shape, materials, structure and peculiarities of technique. Descriptive data thus compiled were then compared with the previously extant descriptive data, and the latter accordingly revised.

Descriptive and historical particulars assembled were enlarged by comparisons with similar published and unpublished works, the results of which are manifest, in this catalogue, in the discussion following the description of each piece, and final conclusions written down there were drawn either on the basis of acceptable precedent or of style. A terminal rearrangement was made according to the consequences of this total process, the items within each type-group being ranked, so far as possible, chronologically by centuries and, within each century, alphabetically and geographically by probable country of origin.

Since the first use of jewels was probably magical, as protective amulets, and by extension religious, the cross was chosen as the first type-group. Thus no. 1 in the Catalogue is the earliest item in the collection, the Byzantine porphyry cross and its German, 15th century encasement. It is followed by no. 2, an Italian, mid-16th century cross, and so on. The remaining categories, after crosses, are: pendants with symbols and images of Christ; pendants with the Virgin Mary; other religious pendants; mythological pendants; pendants with mythological creatures; pendants with human figures and portraits; pendants with ships; necklaces and bracelets; lockets; and pharmacies and pomanders.

Behind all this classification two concepts of knowledge were simultaneously at work—sometimes cooperatively, occasionally at cross-purposes. These, an ineradicable part of an art historical training, were the concept of proof by comparison, to show resemblance, or the use of parallels, and the concept of style. What these mean to the cataloguer and how they were used should now be explained.

The Problem of "Proof by Comparison"

The parallel image—as a source of motif, as a means of deciding date and provenance, or as an indicant of stylistic modification—became a definitive part of the art historian's stock-in-trade with

Gustav Pauli's publication of the identity between Marcantonio Raimondi's engraving after Raphael's *Judgment of Paris* and Manet's *Le Déjeuner sur l'herbe* (*Monatsheft für Kunstwissenschaft* I [1908] 53). Since that time the search for "sources" has attained almost the rank of a self-contained and self-justifying discipline.

This method begins with certain premises which are, significantly, the outcome of Freudian theory on the one hand, and the art historian's generally lexicographic approach on the other. The first premise is what might be called "the premise of the subconscious repertory." It assumes that where two similar works exist, the antecedent one must somehow have been seen and stored up in the mind of the maker of the second, and not by any means deliberately.

The second premise might be called "the premise of willful duplication." It assumes that where two similar works exist, the antecedent one was known to, and consciously used by, the maker of the second. Given the parallel as both unconscious and conscious source, a case for the essential eclecticism of the artist is pretty well made, and both assumptions extend into the doctrine that *any* work must have its previous parallel, which can be found if only the search is dogged enough and the material extant.

It is not to be denied that there are hundreds of appropriations, both unwitting and calculated, which may be useful in deducing a tendency of mind, locating a place of origin, or verifying a date. Yet the overvaluation of the parallel has led to an equal number of instances in which the information "confirmed" is at best irrelevant and at worst spurious. These cases arise because both "the premise of the subconscious repertory" and "the premise of willful duplication" carry with them other subordinate premises which, when taken too seriously, invite great trouble. One of these is the supposition that a given "source," no matter how trivial, must somehow have been sufficiently important in its time to make itself felt immediately. Viewed a different way, the same supposition can be used to "prove" an artist's preoccupation with trivia. Another subordinate premise—probably the most harmful of all—assumes that there is no room in the world of imagery for coincidence or independent enterprise leading to similitudes. This can beget the rashest and most extravagant theses: connections between isolated and distant cultures, the existence of secret cults on a world-wide scale, submerged continents and galactic traumas.

And the cardinal difficulty is that no matter which premise is followed, the existence of a parallel is too frequently left to stand as a fact affirmed, without adhering to the prime rule of evidence: that unless an unmistakable connection can be demonstrated, the intimation of pertinence is invalid.

Parallels do have their uses; the cataloguer has employed them, if not indiscriminately, at least as welcome adjuncts. But under what circumstances and by what rule of thumb?

The rule of thumb applied in the discussions of the pieces makes use of the parallel when: a) a particular composition is elaborate and peculiar enough to suggest a special origin outside tradition, convention or accident; b) the secondary object cited serves conspicuously to uphold all the other evidence cited; c) the parallel cited is a "key monument" to which the piece discussed bears so marked a stylistic and technical relation as to be largely beyond dispute.

No. 29, the interior carving of a boxwood *noix* and its parallel, a page of illustrations from the *Biblia Pauperum*, may be used as an example of a) above. Here we have four highly compressed scenes ("The Nativity," "Moses and the Burning Bush," "Gideon and the Fleece" and the "Flowering of Aaron's Rod") with specific peculiarities (i.e., Gideon's armor), the conjunction of which is singular and presumably beyond the unaided invention of the woodcarver. Since the same scenes, with the same conjunction of peculiarities, appear on a single page of a well-known and widely disseminated work of the time, there is a plausible inference that the woodcarver utilized illustrations from the *Biblia Pauperum*, or something very like it, as his model. The conclusion, however, remains no more than an inference and no more than admissable.

Again, as an example of b) above, the similarity of type between the bracelets, no. 61, and those worn by the sitter in the portrait in the Dayton Art Institute, *inter alia*, serves as a corroboration of authenticity, provenance and date.

Finally, as an example of c) above, the use of the "Averbode Cross" in reference to no. 5, is compelled by the shape, the modeling, the disposition of motifs, and the color and qualities of the opaque and translucent enamel. Even here, the existence also of Spanish parallels makes the use of the "Averbode Cross" conditional rather than absolute.

The use of the parallel—a use, it must be insisted, to be applied in art history always with marked abstemiousness—is most convenient in defining what could be called "areas of plausibility." For instance, it is reasonable to suppose that most of the objects from the Treasury of the Virgen del Pilar at Saragossa are Spanish and probably locally manufactured, since the majority of pilgrims were Spanish and their offerings, rather than carried from afar in dangerous times, would have been purchased on the site. Thus a piece similar in type and technique to one from this treasury can be called "Probably Spanish." The singularly agitated realism of some Munich goldsmiths of the late 16th century, as illustrated in the *Hausaltar* of Duke Albert V of Bavaria, is not a prevalent turn of mind. Thus a piece similar in type and technique can be called "Probably South German." But unless the scholar can document a connection between object and parallel, artist and source, and document the connection according to rules of evidence that would be acceptable in a tribunal, he should exploit the parallel only as circumstantial at best, and *never* as the basis of his case.

The often *suggestive* value of parallels—probing in several directions in quest of documentation—goes without saying. But if the scholar is to postulate a concurrent influence, one which will serve as a norm against which objects can be compared and accepted or rejected, he will be far more precise if he engages the principles of style.

The Problem of Style

No word in the art historian's vocabulary is more heterogeneously applied or more flexibly interpreted than "style." Meyer Schapiro's definitive essay ("Style," in *Anthropology Today, An Encyclopedic Inventory*, edited by A. L. Kroeber, Chicago, 1953, pp. 287–312) examines the semantic and historic variants of the word with his familiar profundity of reference and proportion of thought. Somewhat too complex for general use, the essay contains among its opening statements the following: "For the synthesizing historian of culture or the philosopher of history, the style is a manifestation of the culture as a whole, the visible sign of its unity. The style reflects or projects the 'inner form' of collective thinking and feeling." This description is almost a paraphrase of the definition of style which the cataloguer considers the simplest and most successful. It is Le Corbusier's, *Le style, c'est une unité de principe qui anime toutes les oeuvres d'une époque et qui resulte d'une esprit caractérisé*. ("Style is a unity of principle which animates all the works of an epoch, and which is the result of distinguishing idea." From *Vers une Architecture*.)

The crucial terms are "unity of principle" and "distinguishing idea." If "unity of principle" is taken to signify *formal bases*, the epochs during which *all* works were activated by a given set of shapes are few. A true and plenary style is a rare phenomenon. In Western European art there are only three: the Hellenic of the 5th century B.C. (circle, triangle and right angle and their three-dimensional extensions); the High Gothic (the ogive; horizontal and vertical lines); and the Baroque (the spiral, the ellipse and the X-cross). Strictly speaking no unity of principle or formal basis animates all the works of the Roman, the Byzantine or the Romanesque epochs, let alone the 18th and 19th centuries. Yet the usage of "Byzantine style," "Romanesque style," "Rococo style," among others, is so firmly established that a unilateral effort to revise it would be fruitless and confusing. To accommodate custom we must introduce a sub-category, the "secondary style," in which a unity of principle or specific formal basis activates *most* but not all of the works of an epoch. These "secondary styles" are sufficiently circumscribed by visual habit and art historical convention to be recognized and distinguished one from another even by the layman without indoctrination or diagrammatic analysis.

On the other hand, epochs having no unity of principle whatever are said to have a "style," i.e., the Renaissance. Further, an individual artist's mode or idiom, which may be wholly at odds with that of his surroundings or generation, is also called his "style," as the "style" of Cézanne, of Aubrey Beardsley or of Caravaggio.

A single word should never mean so many things at once, the meanings being dependent upon context and illustration. The outcome is messy semantics or a surfeit of qualifications. In order to be more exact, we can resort to etymology again.

Let us bear in mind that "style" comes from the Latin *stilus*, the writing implement used to impress words upon a soft tablet. It is, thus, the instrument, the mechanism, the "unity of principle" by which the whole surface of the tablet is effected and the total presented to the mind. But different scribes, wielding the same *stilus*, will write in different ways, in diverse, personal scripts. Their "manner" (*manus* = "hand") rather than their "style" will separate one from another. We should discriminate then between "style" and "manner." "Style" should refer unmistakably to an epochal unity of principle (either primary or secondary), the formal bases of which are crisp and conspicuous. "Manner" should refer to an individual mode or idiom, at most employed by a group of artisans or peculiar to a locality. Baroque *style* is to be understood as a general, all-pervading design organized according to specific geometric formulae and *only* according to these formulae. The *manner* of Holbein, Birckenhulz, Mignot or whoever, is to be understood as the artist's private and characteristic handwriting. The cataloguer has tried to adhere consistently to this personal but serviceable distinction.

In doing so, he has occasionally collided with an accessory art historical muddle, the outgrowth of the profession's imprecision in respect to the constitution of style. This may be alluded to in a descriptive term, such as "baroque," which, however, should be restricted in its application to denote only the presence of certain fundamental forms (*unité de principe*; spiral, ellipse and X-cross) and their controlling idea (*esprit caractérisé*; the post-Tridentine subjugation of the will to Roman Catholic authority). The word baroque, nonetheless, is used convertibly as a chronological term synonymous with "17th Century." According to such misusage, Versailles, Vermeer and Velasquez are all "Baroque." Our purpose here is not to provoke a wrangle over hermeneutics, but in a field where at least relative verity depends to so great an extent upon stylistic discernment, it is urgent that the indefinite be delimited and the equivocal be resolved. Thus, in addition to the brief commentary just concluded, a practical explanation of method may be helpful.

Three Stylistic Analyses

As illustrations of method, let us take three objects in the collection, preferably three controversial and diverting objects, the critique of which is decisively a stylistic one. These can be nos. 3, 24 and 42.

The method stresses, in each case, the "unity of principle" and the "controlling idea" of the period to which the object has hitherto been assigned, and the "unity of principle" and the "controlling idea" of the period to which the cataloguer prefers to assign it. The findings are both objective and subjective, but severe and sober-minded effort has (it is hoped) made the detached and measurable outweigh the interpretive.

The agate cameo, no. 42, presents a male figure with assorted attributes of divinity—a figure which, because of its general demeanor and the understandable predispositions of scholars, has been regarded as a Roman production of the Julio-Claudian period. If one examines for "unity of principle" a series of Julio-Claudian cameos (Babelon [1897] pp. 105–145, nos. 232–287; Fürtwängler [1900] pp. 316–325; Walters [1926] p. 339) concentrating upon the largest, most carefully worked and securely dated, one soon discerns that a controlling formal basis is, on the whole, lacking. The compositions of both the "Gemma Augustea" and the portrait cameo of Claudius, Agrippina the Younger, Germanicus and Agrippina the Elder in the Kunsthistorisches Museum, Vienna, are not subordinated to a single geometric shape or combination of shapes. The eye moves episodically, at random, from one particular to another. The area of both cameos is filled promiscuously with figures major and minor and ancillary details, without subordination and selection exercised according to a regulating form.

On the other hand, there is a "controlling idea," yet it is not such as to lend itself to selective handling. It is historical, in the literal sense a record, a commemoration of as many particulars, physical and symbolic, as possible. This accounts for the precision and distinctness of the modeling: in the Vienna portrait cameo the facial traits of that not ill-favored family are vividly rendered, with no reduction either in the promenence given the numerous sacred accessories.

The Gutman cameo is of different cast in all respects.

The ellipse containing the figures is accentuated by not one but two borders so that, from the onset, sight is ruled by a paramount geometric shape. Within this, surrounded by vacant area, are posed the human figure and the eagle. The former, despite his bulk, assumes a lissome, Praxitelean stance—an attenuated S-curve. The line of the eagle's turned neck, the aegis, the bent left arm and the profile produces a second, reverse S-curve which, in combination with the first, amounts to a helix. By taking the lines made by the thunderbolt (?) and the inside profile of the left leg, and the almost straight lower edge of the aegis, one might with some latitude impose an X-cross on the helix, completing the fundamental repertory of Baroque geometry. The "unity of principle" is clear. The "controlling idea" is equally different from that of a Julio-Claudian work. It is pictorial, a single concept carried out in accordance with a theory rather than a concentration of memoranda. Modeling has been softened and the profile depersonalized. The sacred attributes so essential to identification have been abridged. We have, then, a work which, from its total organization and technique, is irreconcilable with its traditional origin. Since

22

the figure would be nude were the piece Hellenistic, there is only one other period to which it can conform, that of the Baroque of about 1630, or exactly the time when the collections of Thomas Howard (ca. 1585–1646) at Arundel House were in their prime. The cameo is not, of course, a full-fledged Baroque work. It is an archaeological effort inadvertently dominated by the style of its time. Now that the slanted vision of its contemporaries has been corrected, the style is more apparent than the ostensible source.

In our second example, the baroque pearl pendant with St. Jerome (no. 24), the application of our diagnostic formula is not so all-inclusive. Nonetheless, the determination of a "unity of principle" or controlling geometric shape which can be fixed in time and taken as the imprint of an attitude is opportune here, too.

The piece has been given without reservation to the end of the 16th century. The basic shape of the frame (the pearl itself does not concern us) is a somewhat compressed or "Cartesian" oval. This is accented, on the front, by four decorative bands, each ending in tight volutes at either end. The shape and its analogues, such as the "Limaçon of Pascal" or conchoid of a circle, are not Baroque figures even though their discovery and discussion date from the first half of the 17th century. They are, at their purest, early Rococo. They begin to occur about 1712, in the project for the altar of Saint-Jacques de la Boucherie, by Gilles-Marie Oppenord (Kimball [1943] fig. 107), in Germain Boffrand's decorations in the Hotel de Villars, about 1716 (*ibid.*, figs. 154–155), in François-Antoine Vasse's projects for the Hotel de Toulouse, 1718 (*ibid.*, fig. 125) and elsewhere. The device of marking off the figure into four arcs separated by volutes can be seen in Armand-Claude Mollet's designs for the Hotel d'Evreux (Palais d'Elysée) 1720 (*ibid.*, figs. 159–161). In Spain, the Cartesian oval was apparently known to the Churrigueras. It was employed in the (now demolished) patio of the cloister of Santo Tomás in Madrid, a work of the last third of the 17th century, by José Jiménez Donosa and José Churriguera (cf., *Arte* [1919] pl. 52) but it does not occur as a familiar frame or cartouche until after the rebuilding of Aranjuez in 1727. The figures remain symmetrical until about 1730, when they become asymmetrical in accordance with the *genre pittoresque*, Coypel's *Un choix piquant et singulier des effets de la nature*.

The "controlling idea" behind this shift from the uncompounded bases of French 17th century classicism to the special curves of the Rococo during the Regency (1715–1723) and the *style régence* (1715–ca. 1730) was more than the mood of "effrontery, innovations and frivolous immorality" which is the hackneyed synopsis of the period. It was rather a resurgence of artistic freedom, away from rules, philistine imitation, and *a priori* principles toward sensibility and invention. *Un ouvrage peut être mauvais sans qu'il y ait des fautes contre les règles, comme un ouvrage plein de fautes contre les règles, peut être un ouvrage excellent.* ("A work can be bad even though it does not break the rules, just as a work that breaks all the rules can be outstanding.") (Jean Baptiste, Abbé Dubos [1670–1742] *Réflexions critiques sur la poésie et la peinture*, 1719, p. 114). Yet the shape to which we allude commands precedent only for a time: by 1728, in the designs of Meissonier, it has become deliriously irregular and congested.

The third piece, no. 3, is one in which stylistic organization involves the use of space rather than geometrical shape, the use of space being an inescapable consequence of technical virtuosity. In this the work bears to the architectonic pendants of the late 16th century the same relation that Flamboyant style does to the Gothic.

Here the voids between solids are ampler and more complex than the solids defining them. The structure is minimal: each component is exhibited in three dimensions from every possible line of sight. The craftsman who made the pendant was technically cunning in the highest degree. There are no detectable flaws or crudities even under a forty-power lens: competence is evident from all angles, and the angles are multiplied by the number of open intervals. Thus the basis of composition that constitutes the style to which the piece can be related is the intricate use of the space through which a multitude of details is seen.

The direction of the late 16th century German current in which the pendant belongs can be made out in architecture, in graphics and in the decorative arts. It can be seen in the Grottenhof of the Alte Residenz in Munich (ca. 1586) in which the fenestration is separated by ample niches with free-standing figures. Jost Amman's (1539–1591) print of Gaspar de Coligny (1573) (Hollstein, I, 9) is at first sight an over-enriched confection in which allegorical figures, still life, decorative motifs, architecture and the portrait itself are all scrambled together. But on closer scrutiny the welter is seen to be singularly intelligible. The shading is handled with such prodigious skill that the viewer realizes that were the print a work in three dimensions, it could be *seen through* and visually integrated by means of the space rather than the structure. In the decorative arts this same inclination is seen between about 1570, in the *Hausaltar* of Albert V of Bavaria (see the commentary on no. 3 in this catalogue) or the *Hausaltar* with the Flagellation (Thoma-Hege [1955] fig. 43) ca. 1590 to about 1592, and in a reliquary-monstrance (*ibid.*, figs. 46–47). These intact monuments are our best analogies. Technically, they are awesome. The cohesion, the order imposed upon the deluge of detail, is not due to controlling structure but to their transpicuous fabric: the fact that every line, surface and contour does not inclose space, but is defined by space, gives them their surprising poise.

The pendant, no. 3, is thus at the other end of the stylistic spectrum from the cameo, no. 42. The latter, belonging to a "primary" style, accommodates itself—intentionally or unintentionally—to the universal geometric foundations. The former, belonging to an interim period and somewhat freakish circumstances, nonetheless can be analyzed according to the same principles: the "unity of principle" is spacial access to every aspect; the "controlling idea" is technical bravura. Neither can be wholly experienced without the other.

On Materials and Design

In periods such as our own, as part of the extension of anomy, the artist often legislates for himself laws in respect to the use of materials and the practice of design which, having no other antecedents than the artist's will to self-expression, cannot be applied to any works from another hand. In defiance of the institutional and the traditional, the artist becomes plaintiff and defendant, attorney, jury and judge, with his case a closed hearing inarguable save on rigorously special and personal rationalizations. Since it is the predisposition of one period always to ascribe its own drives to whatever other periods it examines historically, this view of the artist-craftsman as autonomous "creator" is liable to affect involuntarily—and perhaps to the disservice of pleasure—the vision of whoever may look upon a jewel from a different time. To counteract this bias, the reader may be reminded of some fundamentals which should strengthen his enjoyment even as they modify his prejudices.

A jewel is first of all a material or combination of materials, each of which has a constitution that cannot be mistreated without corrupting the object, the maker and the observer. The character of a

24

material, its "temperament," so to speak, is not to be mastered by theory, by reading or hearsay, or by any procedure other than direct experience. The machine has so universally intruded itself between our hands and our natural heritage that the manual exploration of substances—once a common adventure—has all but vanished. Those to whom a jewel presents a sort of miracle unconnected with physical processes must, if they can, project themselves back into a world where gold and silver, gems and enamel, the casting and carving of metals and stone, were accessible to the senses from mine to merchant. Interlocking operations made possible an average intimacy with handcraft that pervaded most of society. The peeress with her embroidery frame was kinswoman to the tapestry weaver at her loom; the scribe of the market place was cousin to the illuminator, the printer, the vendor of quills and the Master of the Rolls. Thus to examine a jewel is also to examine substances and a working-out of possibilities which were recognized and comprehended even by those who had not mastered them. The most important of these materials should now be summarized.

Gold, because of its stability, brilliant lustre and wide-spread occurence in native condition, has been for ages the favorite and most valued metal for jewelry. Reef gold, with the metal embedded in a solid matrix, and alluvial gold, freed from auriferous rock by weathering, are the two most common natural forms. Absolutely pure gold is rare; in nature it is combined with variable proportions of silver, which, when increased to 30 percent or 40 percent results in "green gold." Copper intensifies the yellow hue; anything over 8 percent of copper will produce the red gold of the jeweler. "White gold" is a combination of about 25 percent platinum with 75 percent gold.

One of the softest of metals, it is also the most malleable and ductile: it can be beaten to a translucent sheet of not more than 0.0001 mm. and one gram (approximately half an ounce) can be drawn into a wire two miles long. Its mean melting point is 1063 degrees C. In air or water under all conditions of temperature gold is permanent; it cannot be dissolved by nitric, hydrochloric or sulphuric acids, though *aqua regia*, three parts of hydrochloric acid to one part of nitric acid will dissolve it. It readily forms an amalgam with mercury: "fire-gilding" or "wash-gilding" is the process by which this amalgam is used to deposit the gold on another metal, the mercury being sublimed by heat.

Before the exploitation of the New World in the 16th century, the principal European sources of gold were the mines of the Hohe Tauern south of Salzburg, the alluvial deposits of the Meuse and Rhine, and, after 1203–04, the immeasurable loot from Byzantium and the Near East.

For the craftsman no metal is more satisfactory. Its color and hardness can be altered to suit his purposes by the addition of small amounts of readily available metals. Its responsiveness to any kind of tool makes it as sensitive to total psychological affect as the paper and pencil of the draftsman. It is thus the material *in excelsis* of the jeweler, for it will not only react to but enhance both his aptitudes and the substances he uses to supplement the whole.

Silver, called "Luna" or "Diana" by the alchemists and assigned by them the symbol of the crescent moon, in its pure state is perfectly white and, except gold, the most malleable and ductile of all metals. Somewhat harder than gold when pure, it is still too soft for jewelry or coinage and must be hardened by alloying it with copper measured in parts of silver in 1,000 parts of the alloy. "Sterling" silver is 925 parts of silver to 75 parts of copper, or 92.5 percent and 7.5 percent. The mixture increases the metal's toughness, hardness and fusibility without appreciably changing the color or rendering it brittle.

"Native silver" is occasionally found in the metallic state, but unlike gold must most often be extracted from its ores along with other elements (commonly sulphur, arsenic and antimony). Silver-lead ore was mined in Asia Minor at Hissarlik in the Troad probably as early as 2500 B.C.; the mines at Laurion in Attica were opened about 1000 B.C., and are worked even today for lead, manganese and cadmium. During Roman times most of European silver came from Spain. Two causes led to the decline of the use of Spanish silver in the Middle Ages: the Islamic conquest of the Peninsula and the increased depth of the mines, made uninhabitable by the presence of sulphur-dioxide fumes. These circumstances brought about the discovery and exploitation, as early as the 10th century, of mines in Germany and Austria, and these, in turn, were supplanted by those of the New World, the mines at Potosí in Bolivia having been opened in 1545. From this source alone, between 1547 and 1864, the total output has been valued at more than $2,000,000,000.

While in its pure state silver is not subject to oxidation and will remain bright indefinitely in pure air, it will tarnish rapidly if exposed to sulphides or chlorides. This tendency (so irksome to the housewife and the museum curator) is, for the maker of jewels, one of its more appealing features. Any recess in the surface will shortly become tarnished, giving to the projecting parts, which are likely to be kept bright by friction, a distinctness and contrast not to be obtained from the uniform brilliance of gold. For two-dimensional linear decoration and three-dimensional sculpturesque effect silver is, for this reason, to be preferred to its nobler companion. With a melting point (960.5 C.) somewhat lower than gold (1063 C.), silver is proportionately easier to cast, and its affinity to mercury makes the process of gilding economically manageable and technically uncomplicated.

Enamel—the substance with which so many jewels are further embellished—is simply a translucent or opaque vitreous glaze upon a metallic surface. The basis of all enamel is a combination of silica, minium (red oxide of lead) and potash, called "flux," colored by oxides of metals and, when desired, made opaque by the addition of calx, a mixture of calcined tin and lead. The flux and its coloring compounds having been pulverized to a fine powder (frit), the metal surface is thoroughly cleaned and the frit placed upon it. Introduced into the furnace, the piece remains until the enamel fuses into a shiny mass (usually not more than a few minutes time is necessary). Each color, opaque or translucent, will have a different fusing point: the number of firings of a single piece may therefore by many, carefully graded downward in furnace temperature and firing time from the highest to the lowest.

Champlevé enameling makes use of troughs chiseled into the metal bed-plate, the metal line or dike between them forming the outline and interior bands of the design. The troughs being filled with frit, this is then fused and the irregular surface is polished down to an even plane.

Cloisonné enameling makes use of thin bands or *cloisons* of metal soldered to the plate or fixed to it by the enamel itself. These form cells identical with those of a *champlevé* piece, save that the thinness and flexibility of the band permit an extraordinary variegation of internal design and color pattern. The processes of filling with frit and firing are the same as in *champlevé* enameling.

Basse-taille enamel involves the engraving and carving of a design in the metal bed-plate beneath the surface; this then shows through the translucent enamel fluxed upon it as an engraving or a relief sculpture would show through a colored window.

Painted enamels, usually upon copper, are carried out by first firing on a slightly domed sheet a single ground color, upon which the design is painted with a brush loaded with frit bound with oil of lavender.

26

Of the innumerable gems—precious, semi-precious and pretended—that enrich the gold, silver and enamel, only the most notable can be mentioned here.

The diamond, that empress regnant of all gem stones, is first known in the west as *Adamas*, "the invincible," from a reference in Manilius (fl. ca. 9 A.D.), *Sic Adamas, punctum lapidis; pretiosor auro* ("Thus the diamond, a lozenge of stone, more precious than gold"). Pliny the Elder (ca. 23–79 A.D.) described six varieties, of which one, an octahedral crystal, is probably the true Indian alluvial stone, from the eastern side of the Deccan plateau. The word *adamas*, by a series of corruptions, became *adamant*, *diamaunt*, *diamant* and *diamond*. It is the only gem composed of a single element, carbon; though the most esteemed are the wholly colorless they may be colored by impurities grey, brown, yellow, red, green, blue and even black. Owing to its natural crystalline shape, the most commonplace early use of diamonds was a four-sided pyramid, the octahedron having been cut in half. By the 14th century the flat side had been inverted and chamfered, to produce a table-cut with facets beneath, superior in magnificence and fire to the tapering-cut. Before about 1740, when the Brazilian mines of Minas Geraes became important, all important European diamonds must have been of Indian origin, even though overlaid with legendary accretions. Sinbad's "Valley of the Diamonds," where eagles rose to flight carrying diamonds adhering to meat thrown on the ground, probably has its source in the former Indian custom of sacrificing cattle at the opening of a new mine, to propitiate evil spirits: vultures and birds of prey, falling on the carcasses, would give rise to such a legend. By the second half of the 15th century the diamond cutters of the Low Countries were already famous; the district of Paris known as "La Courarie" was their home, and by 1497 there were diamond cutters in Lyons.

The emerald, from the Greek σμάραγδος (*smaragdus, smaraldus, esmeraude, esmeralde*), is a bright green variety of beryl, a silicate of beryllium and aluminum, crystallizing hexagonally; its color is probably due to the presence of chromium. The stone occurs embedded (one of its Sanskrit names, *acmagarbhaja*, means "freed from the rock") in a matrix frequently of mica-schist, talc-schist and calcite. The principal ancient sources were Egyptian, from the areas of the Jebel Zabara and the Jebel Sikait, proximate to the Red Sea east of Aswan, rediscovered by the French traveler Caillaud in 1816–1817. The gems were exported from the city of Berenike, founded in 275 B.C. by Ptolemy Philadelphus, and were worked, after the Arab conquest, until the end of the 14th century. These mines, known fancifully also as "Cleopatra's," had probably been worked for centuries prior to the Alexandrian conquest. Huge quantities of the stones came into Spain with the conquest of Peru, but their exact source has never been discovered. Much softer than the diamond (with an index of hardness of 10 for diamond, that of the emerald is 7.5) the emerald is lacking in "fire" and refractive and dispersive qualities: it is therefore cut primarily *en cabochon*, as a table, or even left as a natural prism. Its curative and protective powers were numerous. It was a specific for epileptic convulsions and the "falling sickness"; it hastened childbirth, drove away anxieties and increased eloquence, strengthened the memory and, by changing color, revealed adultery (Johannis Braunii, *De Vestitu Sacerdotum Hebraeorum*, Amsterdam, 1680, p. 659).

The ruby, a red transparent variety of corundum, if of the very limited true Oriental origin from Upper Burma, is the most valuable and the rarest of all gem stones. What pass for, and are generally called "rubies" in much Renaissance jewelry are magnesia spinels of European origin, found along with garnets in the mines of Zoblitz and Greifendorf in Saxony and Meronitz in Bohemia. The deep red almandine garnet, found in the schists of the St. Gotthard and Zillerthal, also substitutes for the true ruby, and the balas (from the OFr. *balais*, Arabic *balakhsh*, from Persian *Badakhshan*, their source) often notable for its huge size (the "Black Prince's ruby," as large as a hen's egg, in the British Imperial State Crown, is a balas) was especially popular in Tudor England. With a hardness of 9 for the true ruby, it may be cut faceted, but for spinels, with a varying hardness of 7.5–8, the table-cut is preferred.

Pearls are lustrous, calcareous concretions of the same substance as "mother of pearl" but without the phenomenon of iridescence, produced principally by the pearl oyster (*Ostrea margaritifera*). The introduction within the shell of any irritating matter will produce a spherical pearl, a *perle bouton*, a "blister" (hollow) pearl, or a "baroque" pearl, as the case may be. Before the opening of the East Indies, almost all pearls used in Europe came from the Persian gulf, the most important beds being off the island of Bahrein. Fresh water or river pearls are produced especially by the species *Unio margaritiferus*, a mollusc particularly prevalent in the principal rivers of Scotland: a breastplate studded with British pearls was dedicated to Venus Genetrix by Julius Ceasar. The number of pearls available for use must have been enormous: the portraits of Queen Elizabeth, such as that of ca. 1575 in the National Portrait Gallery, show her gowns studded with pearls in such profusion that even the heavy embroidery of the fabric is interfered with; the mitres of the Russian Metropolitans are so covered with pearls (from the rivers near Feodosi in the Crimea) that the fabric has disappeared.

A jewel made up of some or all of these components is as much a "work of art" as Michelangelo's *David* or Rembrandt's *The Jewish Bride*. It is as much a work of art as an unadorned melody of Mozart is unquestionably music though of a different kind and objective from the dissonant convergences of *The Rites of Spring*. To be sure, as a *statement*, a jewel may indeed be rudimentary. It will often want complexity of reference and refinement of allusion, even though the plainest jewel is positively labyrinthine in its implications when compared to a work of the contemporary "cool" or "minimal" school, which is extenuated by so much imperious rhetoric. An established snobbery, painful to justify and baffling to account for, now separates into upper and lower classes the "fine" and the "decorative" arts.

The viewer of jewels, who comes to them with an inquisitive vision and pliant opinions, should bear in mind that he can divine their qualities and judge their relative success with some comprehension of the materials also. No esoteric lore is needed. A few suggestions might be made, as a brief *vade mecum*.

Give thought to the metal of which the structure itself is made. If gold, are its malleability, ductility and brilliance externalized in an explicit, intelligible way? If silver, has apt use been made of the contrast between what projects and what recedes, brightness and dark? If there is a combination of the two, are the possible accents and distinctions between yellow and white, between the modulations of shadow and the subtle contradiction of tarnish, so arranged as to enliven and modify each other without antagonism?

Give thought to the enamel, translucent or opaque. If translucent, is the surface even and the body without flaws? Is the hue rich enough to sustain itself while pervaded by the sheen of the metal underneath? Do its translucency and color point up the refraction and color of the gems attached and the opaque enamel adjoining? If opaque, is the texture uniform and the color regularly disposed? In either case, applied to the metal underneath, does the enamel enhance the underlying form?

Give thought to the gems, their refraction and color primarily. Are they so cut as to be either prismatic or to absorb light for interior luminosity? Are their shapes proper to their crystalline structure?

Are the rotundity and iridescence of a pearl set to work in seemly connection with the planes and angles of the adjacent stones?

And are all the forms—abstract, natural or human—assembled not only in accordance with their material properties but in accordance with a well-conducted scheme of design?

With the introduction of the word "design" we must have recourse to etymology again. It comes into English from the French *désigner, dessein*, Italian *disegno, disegnare*, from the Latin *de + signare*, "to mark out," and it means, strictly, the marking out of the elements—material, abstract and figurative— of a composition so that they will all be under control and compatible with each other. It is the conscious means by which the artist gives order to what he makes: an order which will attract the beholder at the outset, rally his interest throughout a complete exploration of the parts, and point to and confirm the content of the whole.

The design, the "marking out" of a jewel, must be thought of as a process part sculptural, part planometric, part linear, part coloristic. In the Renaissance, a goldsmith's training was considered particularly advantageous in respect to linear discipline and definition of style. Lorenzo Ghiberti (1378–1455) began his career under the goldsmith Bartoluccio di Michele; Filippo Brunelleschi's (1377–1446) apprenticeship was probably to Benincasa Lotti; Botticelli (1444?–1510) served under the "battiloro" Antonio Filipepi; Antonio Pollaiuolo (1433–1498) was also a pupil of Bartoluccio di Michele; Andrea Verocchio (1436–1488) took his name from his first teacher, Giuliano de' Verocchio, "of the true eye"; Albrecht Dürer (1471–1528) was son and grandson of a goldsmith; as late as the 16th century, Baccio Bandinelli (1493–1560) also the son of a goldsmith, trained first for the same profession.

We should not invariably assume that these men left the goldsmith's *bottega* for what would be modern, post-Romantic motives: liberation from restraint and the chase after some "higher" individual utterance. Benvenuto Cellini certainly regarded his life-long profession as no such confinement. The choice to quit one livelihood for another in the arts was probably controlled as much then as now by two factors: fashion (prestige) and money, and the wobbly rationalizations of our own age may well have been present, though less presumptuously, in the Renaissance. A jewel, therefore, is not a work of "self-expression" but its stature is not to be cut down on that account. It may be an exercise in organization, in the building up of a systematic harmony of parts and substances far more complex than that of a painting or a piece of sculpture.

This complexity, which may be figurative or abstract, or both, is the product of a craftsman (the word is used synonymously here with "artist") who began with a drawing, proceeded to a model in wax or wood, cast the separate parts, enameled them, and set and attached the stones, which were either cut to size by a lapidary or embodied, ready-cut, in the first stages of the design. The process is from the linear and two-dimensional to the sculpturesque and architectural, with the coloristic aspect of the whole in view from the beginning, a process which entailed at each stage the personal and manual exertions of the maker. We must, therefore, reverse our present-day concept of specialization, of sub-contracting and fragmentation of labor. To look at a jewel is to look at the three-dimensional result of an operation which began as a drawing and ended often as polychrome sculpture surrounded by architectural structure, not only "invented," but "performed."

The designs for jewelry by Dürer, Holbein, Virgil Solis, Étienne Delaune, Erasmus Hornick, Hans Collaert, Paul Birckenhulz, Daniel Mignot, Étienne Carteron, P. Symony and many others, should be taken (even when, as in Dürer's case, the artist was trained as a goldsmith) as "fantasias," as self-set tests or experiments in the rendering of special themes, rather than as projects from which a goldsmith— himself fully capable of designing his own output—might copy or adapt. At least, so it appears to the writer. For this reason, planographic designs for jewelry have been used with some uneasiness as a means of dating: it is only our opinionated and illusory differentiation between "higher" and "lower" orders of art that forces the assumption that the practitioners of the latter must necessarily have trailed the ingenuity of the former.

A jewel, then, should be penetrated by the eye and put together in the mind: as a synthesis of materials felicitously wrought according to their properties, bringing to light the movement of line, the density of sculpture, the stimulus of colors and the lustre of gems, all performing within a structural ambiance. When so viewed, a jewel is no longer merely decorative, an accessory to costume or an ornamental talisman; it takes its high and rightful place among those scarce and precious fruits of human hands that follow upon a flowering of the spirit.

PARKER LESLEY

Catalogue

Bibliographical references are given simply by a key name with date of publication in parenthesis or brackets, followed by pertinent page and plate numbers. To get the full bibliographical detail, readers should turn to the Bibliography where each work is cited in full in alphabetical order according to the key name.

Dimensions are given in inches, and the numbers in parenthesis which follow are the metrical equivalents expressed in centimeters.

All black and white reproductions are actual size except the larger necklaces, and all details have been enlarged.

Pectoral Crucifix of Porphyry and Silver Gilt

BYZANTINE AND GERMAN   6TH–7TH (OR 8TH–9TH) AND 15TH CENTURIES

The basis of the Cross is an enclosed Cross of Byzantine workmanship, of mottled porphyry with bevelled edges and a single drilled hole at the top. This fits into a silver-gilt lidded case, the lid secured at the top by a simple pin bolt. The back, or lid, has two lancet openings cut through the metal at the top and, in the left and right arms, sixfoil openings within incised squares, through which the porphyry surface of the interior Cross can be seen. The center and lower upright supports a column with Gothic foliation on the base and capital; the column has been soldered to the lid but has since separated for two-thirds of its length. The cast and carved figure of a nimbed Christ, with forearms tied behind His back, looking down to the right and wearing a heavily draped cincture, is soldered to the column. The sides of the case consist of four separate sections corresponding to the arms of the cross. Each consists of a row of small newels, held between bands with two concave channels each. These four sections have been mitred and soldered together at the four inner corners of the case. Again, the inner porphyry Cross is revealed through the interstices of the newels. The front of the case is set within the side frame and held level with it by internal soldered metal brackets. A second openwork composition provides the background for a crucified Christ. At the top, a sixfoil opening is brought within the oblong by four trefoil openings at the corners. Each arm has a short lancet opening and two cusped openings; the bottom arm has two lancet openings, one on either side of the pendant body of Christ. The cast and carved silver-gilt figure of Christ is soldered to the incised flat metal cross.

Height 3¾ (9.5)
Width 1¹⁵⁄₁₆ (4.9)
Published
    D'Otrange (1953) pp. 126–127, ill. nos. I–IV
BMA L.62.15.45
Gutman 1190

This is a most interesting and striking pendant, of considerable historical import. Its date, provenance and the purpose are matters of conjecture. The interior porphyry Cross is likewise problematical, for its austere shape, that of a slightly elongated Cross *patée*, may be paralleled from the 6th through the 12th centuries, but its form would be most accordant either with the 6th and early 7th centuries, or the Iconoclastic Period (726–842). The stone itself, probably *porfido rosso antico* from the Jebel Dhokan on the west coast of the Red Sea, would indicate either an Egypto-Syrian origin prior to 639–641, when the area was cut off from the Eastern Empire by the Arab conquest, or, more likely, a working of material previously obtained. The hole drilled at the top of the Cross may or may not be coeval with its manufacture, and may or may not be for reliquary use.

D'Otrange (1953) introduces a pleasant but hazardous association of ideas respecting the Cross. According to her, it is a *staurothéque* or portable reliquary for a fragment of the True Cross or the Crown of Thorns, the hole being the container of the fragment. Stone was chosen as the material because of the

33

requirements of the Mass, which could be celebrated only on a stone altar containing relics of a martyr. By placing the stone Cross under or on a table, the ministrant would be able to celebrate the rites anywhere. This, in turn, leads to the conclusion that the original owner would have been a *presbyter* or *episcopus*, and that the Cross was carved from a "chip off some shrine of particularly holy renown in Syria, Palestine or Egypt—perhaps the grave of a martyr." Thus D'Otrange. It should be called to mind in connection with her suggestion that the Greek and Latin words most commonly denominating an altar, τράπεζα and *mensa Domini*, clearly refer to a table. From the time of Lactantius (*De origine erroris*, ii, 2) to William of Malmesbury (*Gesta pontif.*, iii, 14) it is certain that altars were often of wood. The hole at the top could have been drilled at any time then or later for the insertion of a fixed metal ring or loop.

On the grounds of the shape of the Cross and its material, it may be called either Egypto-Syrian, 6th or 7th century, or Byzantine, 8th or 9th century. The exterior silver-gilt housing is more outspoken. While the evidence offered by parallels with the major arts must be used with hesitation (cf., *Introduction*, p. 19), the sixfoil "windows" with their surrounding cusps seem to be a definitely late-Gothic, 15th century, and predominantly German type, comparable with a range of examples from those of the Franciscan Church at Salzburg, begun 1408, to those of the aisle windows of St. Barbara's, Kuttenberg, of 1512. The modelling of the two figures of Christ is finer than, but consonant with, German pilgrim's pendants in the Melvin Gutman Collection (nos. 1313 d, e and g) of the same century. D'Otrange is very sagacious in suggesting that the two aspects of Christ represent bodily and spiritual agony. This would be in accord with the ideals of the Franciscan Observant reform of the 15th century in Germany.

2 Pectoral Crucifix of Rock Crystal, Gold, Enamel and Pearls

ITALIAN   MID-16TH CENTURY

The Cross proper is a simple unflawed slab of rock crystal with beveled edges, on one side of which a Crucifix with titulus and skull has been intaglio-cut by the wheel, with the exception of the eyes of the skull, which are tubular-drilled. The crystal Cross is surrounded by a cast and carved gold frame consisting of a flat band to which has been soldered a high torus molding with beading filled with a bluish-gray enamel. At the four ends of the Cross are fleur-de-lis volutes filled with opaque black and greenish-white enamel, each with two translucent blue enamel pellets. The Cross is held in position on both sides by prongs. Two pin-fastened seed pearls are suspended from the arms; a large pin-fastened pearl is suspended from the foot.

Height 3¾ (9.6)
Width 2⅜ (6)
Exhibited
    Detroit Institute of Arts (1958–1959)
Published
    Detroit (1958) no. 360
BMA L.62.15.217
Gutman 1162

This strikingly pure crystal is appropriately set in a delicate frame, the finesse of which, however, contrasts with the cutting of the intaglio. This discrepancy raises the questions of whether crystal and intaglio are coeval with the frame, or whether the cutting of the intaglio was undertaken as an alteration or improvement. For example, the INRI of the titulus reads IИRI, with the N not designed to read properly from the front. Any determination which would fix the date and provenance securely is therefore to be based only on the frame, and the mid-sixteenth century Italian source suggested by its form awaits further confirmation.

3   Pendant Crucifix of Gold, Enamel, Rubies and Pearls

SOUTH GERMAN (BAVARIAN?)   CA. 1570   *Color plate facing page 42*

The foundation is an intricately worked, cast, carved and tooled framework of a Cross and iconographical emblems. This base consists of a Cross *fleury*, the ends of which are floriated enamels of translucent red, green, blue, and opaque white, black and yellow. To the left, behind Dismas (on the right hand of Christ) are a gold ladder, the palm of martyrdom enameled in translucent green, and the spokes of a wheel (?). On the right, behind Gestas, is a similar gold ladder, a translucent blue enameled spiral column surmounted by an opaque white enameled cock, the fasciae, and three gold dice with opaque black enamel pips. Attached to the base of this background are the opaque white enamel figures of the two thieves bound to a tan enameled Cross, cast, carved and tooled from a single piece. On the left, Dismas, the good thief, slightly elevated above his companion, turns his head toward Christ. On the right, Gestas, the bad thief, whose legs dangle without support, looks downward. The figure of Christ, enameled with opaque white and translucent green, is attached to a Latin Cross, bolted through the background ensemble. At the ends of the arms and at the head of the Cross are bolted three rectangular table-cut rubies in collet mounts with white opaque enamel droplets at the base. At the base of the Crosses is bolted a series of three rectangular table-cut rubies in collet mounts with white opaque enamel droplets and beneath this, bolted separately, is a triangular collet-mounted table-cut ruby with white enamel droplets. Suspended from the bottom of the background is a single pearl. The back of the background Cross *fleury* is enameled in white *champlevé* enamel in a pattern of ovals, rectangles and curls. The translucent green, red and blue enamel of the floriation and iconographical motifs of the face is carried through on the back.

Height 2⁹⁄₁₆ (6.4)
Width 1½ (3.8)
Collection
     Kunsthaus, Zürich
Published
     von Falke (1928) p. 105, no. 612, ill. pl. 120
BMA L.62.15.5
Gutman unnumbered

The stylistic characteristics of this splendid piece are three: 1) extreme realism with an almost incredible microscopic scale (*viz.*, the pips of the dice and the cock on the column); 2) contrast between highly modelled, even if minute figures, and open space interrupted by frame and embellishments; 3) the decoration of the back. A very similar composition of the Crucifixion, without the two thieves but with the implements of the Passion, is to be found in the Louvre, Rothschild Bequest (Evans [1953] pl. 81). The present Crucifix was perhaps made during the reign of Emperor Rudolf II and a date of about 1570 would be most reasonable on the basis of style. Von Falke's dating of "about 1600" seems at least twenty-five years too late.

Two well-known works are worth citing here for identity of approach, although their style is quite different. A Crucifix in the Schatzkammer of the Residenz, Munich (R.K. 63; Thoma and Hege [1955] pl. 39) probably from the workshop of Hans Reimer, Munich, about 1570, has the same kind of *corpus* attached to a pierced enamel casing over-lying an ebony cross; this piece was the gift of Anna, wife of Albrecht V, to the Benedictine Abbey at Andech. The "house altar" of Albrecht V of Bavaria in the Residenz (R.K. 155) probably made in Munich about 1570 and in the *Reichen Kapelle* since 1626, also presents, both as a whole and in detail, this same propensity for contrasting closely-worked figures, an intricate gold-and-enamel decoration, and a dark background. When the striking effect of this piece as it might be seen worn upon a heavy satin or brocade is considered, the identity of approach is obvious. Likewise, the decoration of the back bears close resemblances to the openwork Cross in the Residenz, mentioned above.

The realism combined with sumptuousness and an iconography saturated with Counter Reformation symbols would indicate that the piece was made either in Germany or Austria, and the religious climate of Bavaria during the reign of Albrecht V was particularly favorable to such works, for, at first favoring reformers, in 1563 Albrecht announced support of the decrees of the Council of Trent and pressed forward the work of the Counter Reformation until his death in 1579.

4 Pectoral Cross of Gold, Enamel, Emeralds and Pearls

SPANISH OR SOUTH GERMAN   SECOND HALF OF THE 16TH CENTURY

The composition consists of three parts. The first part is an extremely elaborate openwork, cast and carved arrangement of interlocking volutes and arabesques in gold bearing traces of opaque white, blue, black and translucent green enamel. The second part consists of a rectangular, hollow Cross, fused and gold-soldered at the edges to the ends of the arabesques and volutes. The third part consists of six tall pyramidal and rectangular collets, enameled opaque white, black and blue, with seven rectangular, cabochon-cut emeralds, each fastened at the corners by four cusps. The two emeralds at the bottom of the Cross are held within a single mount of two stages. The mounts are held within the hollow frame by clasps; several are movable. Four round, pin-fastened pearls at the outside; pearl within volutes at top. On the reverse, the back of the Cross proper is enameled with an interlaced strapwork pattern and arabesques of translucent green and opaque white, surrounding, in the center, a rosette with traces of opaque blue enamel (and a central gem, now missing?) through which can be seen the four bent and split parts of the peg which hold the square central emerald of the face in place.

Height 3¾ (9.6)
Width 3¹⁄₁₆ (7.8)
Published
    Weinmüller (1962) no. 487, ill. pl. 42
BMA L.62.15.64
Gutman 1455

This piece is, without doubt, at once one of the most virile, robust and finely executed jewels in the Collection. It also occasions difficult problems, for date and provenance of the piece are highly problematical and not by any means conclusive. The vendor catalogued the piece as South German, end of the 16th century. Mr. Gutman is now of the opinion that it is English, of the late 16th century, on the basis of first, the similarity between the fastening of the square central emerald and the "butterfly wing clip" of Tudor English workshop practice (Tait [1962] p. 229) and second, a resemblance between the scroll-work of the outside cross and the designs of Hans Holbein.

The cataloguer differs on objective and subjective grounds. First, the single peg, split into four and bent through a square aperture, is quite different from the two broad flanges, bent over through a thin gold plate. Second, the Holbein designs are essentially graphic, delineatory essays which do not possess the robust construction in depth of the present Cross. The Cross, with its interplay of projecting rectangular and interlocked curved forms is, quite simply, a classical, continental approach not found in English art until Inigo Jones (Evans [1931] II, p. 34). The Tudor jewelry adduced by Mr. Tait is all in relatively low relief, engaging the eye over a total surface. English pieces in this catalogue (nos. 14, 44 and 52) do the same. The present Cross, on the other hand, brings abstract solids and voids into play as a splendid three-dimensional composition. The pyramidal collets of the emeralds, with their cusps holding

the stones and flattening to form a rounded W on each side, seem to be primarily, although not exclusively, a German mannerism of the second half of the 16th century.

  The essential severity of the outer Cross and the absence of any figurative or iconographical symbols point, in the cataloguer's opinion, to a Spanish origin between 1555 and 1580. Davillier (1879) has published (p. 212, pl. 12, fig. 3) the design of a Cross submitted on May 5, 1557, by Pere Pares as a *dessin de maitrise* to the goldsmiths' guild of Barcelona. Here four oblong table-cut stones occupy the two arms, foot and head of the Cross, held in very similar collets, with a square, table-cut stone centered.

  The whole might, indeed, be a late 16th century international composite. Similarly mounted emeralds, in high collets held within a German frame of about 1570, may be seen in a Cross formerly in the Eugen Gutman Collection (von Falke [1912] no. 25). These would easily lend themselves to adaptation within a Spanish tradition. The Austrian-Spanish Hapsburg court of the time would make such a fusion not contradictory. Whatever the outcome of further research on this piece, it will remain one of the most spirited in the Collection.

40

5 Pectoral Cross in Gold, Enamel and Amethysts

FLEMISH OR SPANISH   CA. 1560–1570   *Color plate facing page 42*

The gold Cross, a modified Calvary Cross in shape, the normal three step base replaced by an equilateral triangle, is suspended from a large gold ring at the truncated top. It is cast and carved in a single piece. The ends of the three arms are capped by Ionic cartouches enameled opaque white and blue, and translucent blue and red. The enamel of the top cartouche is almost entirely missing. In the four corners of the arms are rosettes bearing circular buds of translucent blue and red. The central part of the Cross consists of seven stones in six compartments (originally also probably seven, the cross-wall on the long arm showing evidence of having been removed) the compartments made by the slightly inclined exterior wall and its interior divisions. On the sides these compartments are a less finished version of the high mounts seen in no. 48, with corner cusps expanding into swag-like panels. These bear small decorative triangles of opaque light blue enamel. The gems consist of one square table-cut amethyst at the top, two rectangular table-cut amethysts placed horizontally in the arms, two rectangular table-cut amethysts placed vertically in the trunk and a truncated, triangular table-cut amethyst in the base. In the center is a large domed cabochon-cut amethyst. The amethysts do not fit their compartments tightly and all the enclosing walls and cusps clearly have been tampered with. The almost flat reverse surface of the Cross (see color plate facing p. 42) is worked in a charming design of flowers, a vase, a bird, and bands enameled opaque white and black, and translucent red, green and blue. Their materials and colors are almost identical with those used on no. 6, especially on the reverse surface of the latter. This suggests that the backs of these two Crosses may come from the same workshop. The enamel is missing in many sections and the surface is much worn.

Height 2⅝ (6.6)
Width 1¾ (4.4)
Exhibited
   Walters Art Gallery (1948)
   Art Institute of Chicago (1951–1962) RX200/7
BMA L.62.15.77
Gutman 624

The fine workmanship of this Cross is of a distinctly Flemish character, most closely paralleled by the "Averbode Cross" (Rosenberg [1911] figs. 83–84), given to the Premonstratensian Abbey of Averbode by the Abbot Matheus s'Volders in 1562, and the work of Reynere van Jaersfelt (fl. 1533–1579) and the goldsmith Jeronimus Jakobs (fl. after 1560) of Antwerp. Not only is the lush sculpturesque handling of the volutes and of the enamels on the present Cross very like that work, but the composition of the back, though of a more secular scheme, is likewise distinctly analogous. However it should be borne in mind that in 1567, at the very apex of Antwerp's prosperity, Reynere van Jaersfelt became head of the Guild of Saint Luke, and in this position his particular style and workmanship must have been of commanding influence.

On the other hand we have a very similar pendant which offers another parallel: it is a Cross set with table-cut amethysts from the Treasury of the Virgin of the Pillar, Saragossa, in the Victoria and Albert Museum (acc. no. 344-1870; Inventory of Art Objects [1870] p. 32) and indubitably Spanish of the early 17th Century. Further, with the opening of mines in the province of Bahia, Brazil, after the city of Bahia became the capital in 1549, amethysts became not only readily available but, by 1600, popular for protection of the heart against poison and the plague and to give sound sleep (Cardanus, *De subtilitate*, lib. vii, Basileae, 1560, p. 473).

Finally, at the same time the commercial and political connections of the Netherlands with Spain and Portugal were at their height. Indeed, the Florentine, Guicciardini (d. 1589), Tuscan Ambassador in the Netherlands, records that in 1566 the spices and sugar imported from Portugal alone were worth one and a half million ducats. Thus it would not be inconsistent for this Cross to have been made in Antwerp about 1560–1570 and mounted with amethysts from Spain, or indeed made in Antwerp for a Spanish (or Portuguese) client. An alternative, although less likely, is that the piece could have been made in Spain after the most fashionable Flemish design. In any case the date and provenance of this Cross depend upon a weighing of such parallels.

9 6   25

5   3

Pectoral Cross in Gold, Enamel, Diamonds and Pearls

Color plate facing page 42

The base or frame of the Cross is a hollow, wax-cast, carved and punch-tooled Cross *botonée*, the ends of which have been broadened and elaborated into an ensemble of strap scrollings, arabesques, clusters of fruit and cartouches, enameled opaque white, black, dark and light blue, and translucent dark blue, green and red. The unenameled portions have been rendered mat by the overall stippling with an extremely small convex punch. The bottom of this foundation, center, contains a winged *mascaron*, not repeated elsewhere. Three pin-fastened pendant pearls are suspended from the two arms and the bottom. Securely fitted within this foundation, and held in place by tapered cusps at the corners, is a second raised Cross, roughly a Calvary but with added lozenge-shaped ends. The inclined walls are a *champlevé* pattern of stylized canopies and arabesques enameled opaque white, black and green, and translucent red, each section of the wall forming a single compartment. Surmounting the surface are thirteen square and rectangular table-cut collet-mounted diamonds of fine water in pristine frames. On the back, the concavity of the sustaining cross is masked by a cast and carved, slightly concave Cross *botonée* held in place by a single central rivet. The surface, of *champlevé* enamel in opaque white, black, blue and green, and translucent red, blue, green and yellow, has lost much of its filling. The upper arm bears, between arabesques, an unidentifiable black enamel shape above what was apparently an escutcheon superimposed upon a quiver of translucent yellow and a bow and arrow of black and

43

44

white. The side arms are filled with arabesques and two hippocamps. The foot contains a crown, or tiara, above two crossed viols with dolphin volutes beneath. The interior Cross is fastened to the sustaining frame by a central rivet, which passes through a reinforced interior crosspiece and ends in the center of the back plate just described.

Height 3¼ (8.2)
Width 2 (5)
Collections
   Mrs. Huddleston Rogers
   Joseph Brummer
Exhibited
   Art Institute of Chicago (1951–1962) RX200/57
Published
   Brummer Sale (1949) 1, no. 687
BMA L.62.15.125
Gutman 1074

This piece is of exceptional sumptuousness and workmanship, and not lacking in quandaries. In the Brummer sale catalogue it was listed as "Italian or Spanish, XVI Century." The Art Institute of Chicago and Mr. Gutman have designated the outside Cross German, second half of the 16th century, and the interior Cross French, mid-16th century. The cataloguer's opinion differs, in part, from all of these. The problems involve 1) the disposition of the gems of the interior Cross or "encolpion"; 2) the designs employed in the enamel of the walls of this interior Cross; 3) the exterior sustaining Cross; 4) the back of the sustaining Cross. The disposition of the gems is comparable to Spanish predilections (cf. Evans [1953] pl. 106) and early 17th century, rather than before, indicative of the shift of emphasis from enamel to the gems now arriving in greater supply from the East Indies and South America.

The designs of Arnold Lulls, the Dutch jeweler who worked for the Court of James I (cf. Evans [1915] pp. 214–215) display this new accentuation. The designs of the enamel beneath the gems appear to be of the swift, attenuated configuration of Mignot-Carteron tradition of between 1590 and 1620. The build of the outside Cross has, again, the same, though somewhat more enriched, features of the "Averbode Cross" (cf. no. 5). Lastly, the back of the sustaining Cross, which is removable and not consistent with the obverse in the color of its enamels (the yellow and green *basse-taille* enamel in the hippocamps) is neither so exuberant nor so precise as the remainder (but in this respect does correspond so closely with the enamels on the reverse of no. 5 that their origin in the same workshop may be predicated).

The cataloguer's inclination is to assign this Cross to an area in which these disparate influences could be handily united without affectation: Flanders, and specifically Antwerp, between about 1570 and 1600. Such an attribution would at least eliminate the question of where and when a French mid-16th century item and a German late 16th century item could have been combined. Detailed examination convinces the cataloguer that the work is a stylistic composite rather than a junction of two works. A suggested explanation of the backing is that the Cross came into the possession of, or was purchased by, an ecclesiastical dignitary whose escutcheon was added, like a name-plate, very shortly after the completion of the major portions of the piece.

7 Pectoral Cross of Gold, Pearls, Garnets and Enamel

GERMAN   1622

The Cross consists of a hollow, straight-walled gold container into the face of which are set twelve table-cut garnets with emblems of the Passion engraved and enameled in opaque pale blue, white and yellow. These, reading from top to bottom, are: INRI, the robe, crown of thorns, cock, column, lance and sponge, ladder and nails; from left to right: money bag, pincers and hammer, crown of thorns (at crossing), palm and scourge, and dice. Four pin-fastened pearls are set in the angles of the Cross and three more pearls depend from rings at the bottom of the two arms and foot. The back is of opaque black *champlevé* enamel and displays an elaborate working of letters and arabesques into a monogram. At the top, H; beneath this a crown; to the left, CI intertwined; center, GM (?), H (?) E or F, Z and S intertwined with a heart; right Z, on the lower right E, and at the bottom the date 1622.

Height 2¼ (5.8)
Width 1⅟₁₆ (2.2)
Collection
    Mary O'Donoghue, London
BMA L.62.15.218
Gutman 1386

46

The simple, geometric shapes of which this Cross is made are paralleled in costume jewelry represented in German paintings of the 17th century; compare for example the jewels in a portrait ascribed to Michael Conrad Hirt (Hirte, Hirth) (Dayton Art Institute, acc. no. 55.71). A very similar pendant, labelled German, 17th century, is in the Victoria and Albert Museum (Alfred William Hearn Gift, M. 60-1923); that museum's Inventory of Art Objects originally called the pendant Spanish, late 17th century.

On our present Cross, the letter H with the arch in the bar is found engraved on a German whistle and toilette kit of ca. 1535 (Bassermann-Jordan [1909] fig. 130) and in German prints of a somewhat earlier date, as for example in the works of Aldegrever and Binck (Hollstein I, p. 144, no. 7; and IV, p. 23, no. 27). The character of the lettering on the Gutman Cross, the angularity of the numerals and the prevalence of the letter Z, in addition to the use of Bohemian garnets, also fixes the provenance as German.

8   Pectoral Reliquary Crucifix of Gold, Emeralds and Pearls

RUSSIAN   SECOND HALF OF THE 17TH CENTURY

The Cross *botonée* is suspended from a hinged member incised with the *sudarium*, the channels of which have been filled with black pigment (bitumen?). The Cross itself consists of a wall in four sections, soldered together on the inside axillae, and two outside plates, the back soldered to the wall on the outside and the front held in place by rivets. The top plate is incised with a Crucifixion, with Christ suspended from a patriarchal Cross; behind is a walled city with towers. To left and right, nimbed busts of the Virgin and St. John, facing inward; above, a seraph, full-face. The filling of the channels is apparently the same as that used in the hinged member above, but much more worn. At each end of the Cross, a large, table-cut and collet-mounted emerald. The collet of the top emerald is decorated with black enamel dots on opaque white enamel scallops. The collets of the two emeralds on each side bear traces of ovals filled with translucent green enamel. The mount of the bottom emerald is plain. One hundred and five irregularly shaped seed pearls, strung on wire and fastened on the interior through holes in the top plate, form the border. On the back of the top hinged member, in blue paint, the number K-4243. The surface of the back plate is finely engraved over its entirety with a list, in Old Church Slavonic, of the relics contained therein. These are: Part of the Mantle of the Lord, of the Life-giving Wood of the Cross of the Lord, part of the Mantle of the Blessed Virgin, Relics of St. John the Evangelist, Basil the Great, Gregory the Theologian, John Chrysostom, Nicephoras Patriarch of Constantinople, Athanasius and Cyril of Alexandria, Nicholas the Miracle-worker, Tikhon the Miracle-worker, Averkii of Hierapolis, Ambrose of Milan, Peter, Alexei, Jonah and Philip of Moscow, Nikita Bishop of Novgorod, Euphemius Archbishop of Novgorod, John Archbishop of Novgorod, Gurii and Varsonofii of Kazan, John . . . (?) (this last name, undeciphered, consisting of two words is found at the very bottom of the two arms of the Cross. It is engraved in a somewhat smaller lettering and may possibly be the name of the goldsmith); also relics of German of Sviazhsk, Arenii of Tver, Prince Alexander Nevskii, Prince George of Vladimir, Prince Andrei Bogoliubskii, Prince Vsevolod of Pskov, Sergei of Radonezh, Alexander of Svir, Savva the Enlightened, and Zosima of Savatjia-Solovetskii.

Height 4⅜ (11.1)
Width 2⅞ (7.4)
BMA L.62.15.65
Gutman 1202B

This Crucifix and its companion piece (no. 9) sumptuously confirm our provenance and dating. Moreover a photograph of these Crosses, now in Mr. Gutman's possession, bears on the back a signed statement, dated Paris, September 15, 1953, by Serge Ernst, "formerly Associate Curator of the Imperial Ermitage Museum in Saint Petersburg," assigning them to the second half of the 17th century: "The design of the Crucifixion confirms this date: the head of the Lord rests not in the center of the Holy Cross, but somewhat beneath . . . it can be safely assumed that the two crosses were made for one of the

48

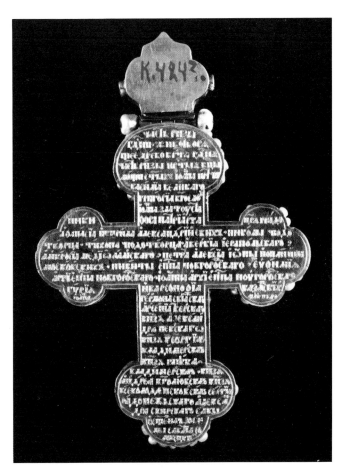

successors of Philaret to the Seat of the Patriarchs of Moscow." Both Crosses contain relics of Alexander Svirskii (or "of Svir"), a holy man who died in 1533, but whose relics were not "discovered" until 1641. This would confirm M. Ernst's date, although in the case he has made, the position of the head of Christ should not have been adduced as substantiating evidence: precisely the same posture occurs, for example, in the Crucifixions embroidered on the cassocks of Photius, Metropolitan of Moscow between 1408 and 1431, in the Kremlin.

49

9 Pectoral Reliquary Crucifix of Gold, Diamonds, Emeralds and Pearls

RUSSIAN   SECOND HALF OF THE 17TH CENTURY

The construction is very similar to no. 8. The wall is made of one single bent gold band soldered to the back on both inside and outside, and joined by an overlap on the left hand side of the bottom arm. The top plate is roughly cast, with the Corpus and Cross carved and punch-tooled, and the remaining floral arabesque pattern punch-tooled from the front surface. A Cross *botonée*, the central portion is occupied by a Crucifixion on a Latin cross with titulus, the head nimbed and inclined to the left. The top arm is filled by a filigree crown of eight diamonds, seven rose-cut and one table-cut. The wires holding the collet mounts of the diamonds are white gold and covered with the remains of opaque white enamel. The crown is attached to the top by wires run through a slot in the upper arm, and, being superimposed on the arabesque pattern, is clearly later than, and a substitute for, the original missing gem. Centered in the left arm, a large collet-mounted, triangular table-cut emerald; in the right arm, a large rectangular table-cut emerald in an oval collet mount. Both of these stones seem to be replacements: the surfaces do not fit the collets, and their security depends on extensive wax grouting. At the base of the Cross, two rectangular table-cut and one triangular rose-cut transparent stones, foil-backed, are mounted as a trefoil Calvary within a somewhat crude single collet mount. In a channel around the edge of the Cross lies a border of one hundred and forty-three irregular seed pearls strung on silk and fastened behind through numerous holes punctured in the channel. The back, which is bordered by a simple rope band, is divided into sections and engraved in Old Church Slavonic with the names of the relics contained therein, as follows (from top to bottom):

Top:
  Mantle of the Lord
Left:
  Mantle of the Blessed Virgin
  Blood of the Lord
Right:
  Wood of the Cross of the Lord
Center:
  Stone from the Sepulchre of the Lord
  Pillar of Christ (the Pillar of the Scourging?)
  Milk of the Blessed Virgin
  Stone from the Sepulchre of the Virgin
  Relic of St. Mary of Egypt
  Left: Relic of the Martyr Agrippina
  Right: Relic of the Martyr Irene

Bottom Arc: . . . (undecipherable) of Spiridon
Arc left: Relic of the Martyr Praskevia
Arc right: Relic of the Martyr Natalia
Left Arm (from end of arm):
  Relic of the Martyr Nikita
  Top: Relic of Anna, Mother of the Virgin
  Center: Relic of St. Martha
  Bottom: Relic of St. Evdokiia
  Relic of St. Matthew the Evangelist
Right Arm (from end of arm):
  Relic of Alexander Svirskii
  Top: Relic of St. Nicholas the Miracle-worker
  Center: Relic of John the Merciful
  Bottom: Relic of Alexander the Man of God
  Relic of Ignatii the Bearer of God

Height 4¼ (10.8)
Width 3⁹⁄₁₆ (9)
BMA L.62.15.66
Gutman 1202A

The dating of this Cross and its companion is discussed above in connection with no. 8. In this present example the Martyr Nikita is not a figure from recent Soviet political history, but the Martyr Nicetus, a Gothic soldier who refused to abjure his faith. St. Nicholas the Miracle-worker is Nicholas, Bishop of Myra in Asia Minor, the original Santa Claus.

10 Pendant Medallion of Gold and Enamel: Christ, Peter and Paul

NORTH ITALIAN (?) GIOVANNI ANTONIO DE' ROSSI (?)   CA. 1570

A cast and carved elliptical frame, suspended from a single ring, consists of four spiral cartouches at the top, bottom, left and right, separating sunken fields each embellished with six dots of opaque dark blue enamel. The top, left and right cartouches are enameled in opaque white and translucent red and green. The bottom cartouche, of more compact shape, is enameled in opaque blue and translucent green. Within the frame is a profile bust of Christ, facing left, unnimbed, with long hair, beard and mantle. The background surrounding the bust is densely punch-tooled to a mat finish. On the reverse, three cartouches at top, left and right, enameled opaque white and blue, and translucent red. Approximately two-thirds of the elliptical field is separated by a horizontal bar, enameled opaque white and translucent blue. Upon this stand, full-faced: St. Peter on the left, with key in left hand; St. Paul on the right, with left hand on hilt of sword. Black enamel inscription between cartouches: left, .S.PETRVS; right, .S.PAVLVS. Beneath the bar, a papal crest with tiara, crossed keys and shield, enameled opaque blue and white, and translucent red and green. Engraved and black enamel inscription between cartouches: right, .PIVS.; left, .V.P(ontifex).M(aximus).

Height 1¹³⁄₁₆ (4.7)
Width 1¼ (3.2)
Collection
  Gerhard Hirsch, Munich
BMA L.62.15.30
Gutman 1460

Pius V, Michele Ghislieri, who authorized this medal, was born January 17, 1504, and became Pope January 7, 1566, dying May 1, 1572. Originally a Dominican monk, he was an ascetic, reformer and fiercely antiprotestant rigorist who strengthened the Holy Office and contributed to the victory at Lepanto, October 6, 1571. The type of Christ here used is one which, united with a great miscellany of reverses, begins with what Hill (1920, pp. 43 ff.) designates the "XPS.REX medal," a Luinesque, unnimbed, draped bust looking to the left, of the early 16th century. The genealogy of the type has been traced with pungent and elegant erudition by Hill: it persists through the career of Gasparo Mola (died January 26, 1640), and extends into the North from Peter Flötner through Valentin Maler at the end of the 16th century.

A description of the complexities found within the province of Papal medals is best left to Hill: "The Papal Mint had a practice, disconcerting to students of numismatic history, of making hybrid medals by attaching a reverse made for one Pope to obverses belonging to another; and it carried this practice to the degree of altering old dies, or making entirely new ones, so that, when the medals struck from them are patinated by age or art, they are frequently very difficult to distinguish from the originals. An almost hopeless confusion arises." (*ibid.*, p. 66)

The head of Christ on the present medal is close to that on one struck by order of Pius V in the sixth year of his reign, 1571–1572, signed by Giovanni Antonio de' Rossi, and this is the basis of our dating; however, it is not distant from all those cited, even the transalpine, and is not listed among those given to the reign of Pius V by Armand (1883, I, 225, nos. 25–29; 226, nos. 30–36; 246, nos. 15–21; 247, no. 22; II, 217, no. 19; III, 105, J, K; 106, a; 117, E; 263, TT to YY; 264, ZZ to III; 265, JJJ) nor by Habich (1923). These medals of Pius V all carry inscriptions beside which the brevity of that on the present example is laudably restrained.

Pendant of Gold, Enamel and Diamonds, with Bloodstone Cameo of Christ

ITALIAN   LATE 16TH CENTURY

The frame, suspended by a single ring from a large, catenary gold loop enameled opaque white and black, consists of a cast and carved gold openwork border of volutes and fleurs-de-lis enameled opaque white and black, and translucent green and red. Eight square silver-gilt collet mounts, containing table-cut foiled diamonds, have been attached at equal points around the frame. The cameo is held in place by forty-three bent cusps separated from a nail-head border by a band of diagonally striped opaque white and painted black enamel. The cameo, a long oval of bloodstone, presents the profile to left of the Man of Sorrows, bearded, with hair to shoulder length. The cameo seems to be entirely chisel-carved, without drill or wheel. The back of the frame has been carved and punch-tooled with swags, cross-hatchings, volutes and rosettes. An oval pin-fastened pearl is suspended from the bottom.

Height 3¹⁄₁₆ (7.7)
Width 1¾ (4.5)
Collections
    Henry Symonds
    Alice de Rothschild
Exhibited
    Walters Art Gallery (1948)
    Art Institute of Chicago (1951–1962) RX200/4
Published
    D'Otrange (1952) p. 69, ill. p. 72
BMA L.62.15.74
Gutman 598

The cameo, expertly done, is straightforward and perfectly consistent with the "devotional" type of the late 16th century seen in nos. 10, 12 and 19. The frame is in three parts. The exterior enameled and jeweled openwork frame is one homogenous casting. The nail-head border within is a second separate part. The enameled and cusped border retaining the cameo is a third. However, the engraving on the back is clearly later in style and quite out of period for the 16th century: it may have been added, as a "beautification," in a subsequent century.

12 Double-Faced Pendant of Gold and Enamel, with Bloodstone Cameo of Christ and Miniature

NORTH ITALIAN   CA. 1580–1600

The oval frame is attached at the top to a single baluster ring with the bulge enameled opaque black. The frame consists of a central convex moulding of volutes, quatrefoils and interlaced rectangles enameled opaque black and white, between plain, slightly beveled mouldings beneath. The obverse contains a bloodstone cameo of the Man of Sorrows, in high relief. The profile, with crown of thorns, beard, mustache and robe, faces right. The small red deposits have been utilized as five gouts of blood between the right ear and temple. The cameo apparently has been cut almost entirely by abrasion, the channels being rounded with tapering ends. In the lower left center at the edge is an old chip much smoothed and worn, perhaps a natural defect in the stone. The reverse contains, under a rock crystal guard, a removable elliptical miniature, oil pigment on copper, with touches of gold. The nimbed and bearded figure is robed in bright red with touches of gold, purple and brown. The right shoulder is bare, and he points with his right hand to the lamb, holding a book in his left. A cross staff also held in the left hand, behind the lamb and the book, bears a white banner with the legend ECCE AGNVS DEI.

Height 2⅝ (6.6)
Width 1¹¹⁄₁₆ (4.3)
Collections
   Sir Francis W. Cook
   Humphrey W. Cook
   Henry Symonds
Exhibited
   Walters Art Gallery (1948)
BMA L.62.15.55
Gutman 597

The cameo is representative of the late 16th century devotional type common to North Italy, discussed in nos. 10 and 11, and there is every reason to believe that the frame, which is agreeable with the cameo, is coeval. The miniature, however, is an intrusion. In order to suit the iconography of Christ, a figure which obviously was once of St. John the Baptist and of orthodox iconography, has since been provided with stigmata and a less savage costume, giving the appearance of a pastiche. The facial type, faintly Luinesque, is too impersonal to permit of confirmation as deriving from a particular artist, or school. The decorative make-up of the frame, with its interlacing of volutes, quatrefoils and rectangles, is also of the type traditionally ascribed to North Italian ateliers.

13   Pendant of Gold and Enamel with Grisaille Enamel Scene and Instruments of the Passion

SPANISH   CA. 1600

The pendant is suspended from a baluster ring, enameled opaque black and white. The basic ellipse is identically enameled on both sides with twenty-five slightly concave compartments, each containing an opaque white quatrefoil on an opaque black background. The wall of each compartment forms, at the rim of the ellipse, the edge of a flattened pyramidal gold ray, there being twenty-four in all. Between these are twenty-five hooked translucent red enamel "flames." An interior elliptical frame with opaque white and black enameling of circles and lozenges encloses a painted grisaille enamel plaque of Christ teaching in the temple (?). The reverse, within a similar frame, presents separate enameled instruments of the Passion: the crown of thorns in translucent red and green enamel; hammer in translucent blue and red, and opaque white enamel; pincers in translucent red and green, and opaque white enamel; column and staff in translucent red, opaque white, yellow and blue; ladder and spear to right in translucent red, opaque yellow and white; IHS monogram; two whips in translucent red and green, and opaque white; and the nails, translucent blue and red. This section of the pendant fits tightly into a cavity now vacant. The grisaille plaque is opaque white enamel on copper, the back of which has been gilded and covered with a transparent flux full of air bubbles. There are minute traces of gold on the throne, the jewel at the woman's breast and the dagger hilt of the male figure on the extreme right. The French owl import mark after 1893 is stamped on the knop of the suspension ring.

Height 3¼ (8.3)
Width 2⅞₆ (6.2)
BMA L.62.15.170
Gutman 627

This radiant piece originally was a reliquary pendant in which the grisaille plaque now present is a substitution, probably for a crystal covering an enclosed relic. The serrated frame with its brilliant, if summary, enamel may be paralleled in any number of indubitably Spanish works (Johnson [1962] nos. 4, 6 and 19; von Falke [1928] nos. 595, 599 and 601).

Philip III's sumptuary decree of 1600, restricting the use of precious metal and gems for decorating costumes, the rise of the Dutch lapidaries and consequent decline of this craft in Spain, re-enforced by the expulsion of the Christianized Moors in 1610, the mystical tendencies displayed in the writings of Luis de Granada (1504–1588), St. Teresa (1515–1582) and especially St. John of the Cross (1542–1591), whose *Obras espirituales* were published in 1618, as well as the progressive enfeeblement of the empire, all conspire to turn artisans away from high finish of technique and inspire them to accentuate the devotional role of jewelry. The similarity of so many of these objects suggests a common place of manufacture: perhaps Valladolid, where the court of Philip III was established until moving to Madrid in 1605.

14   Pendant IHS Trigram in Gold, Enamel, Rubies and Pearls

SPANISH OR ENGLISH   CA. 1600–1620

The pendant consists of a cast and carved framework of the trigram of Christ, the initials IHS with Cross above and the sacred heart at the bottom, interlaced with scrollwork and flowers. The fixed ring emerges from the top of the Cross, which is embellished with six table-cut rubies in collet mounts and two pearls, pin-fastened in the axillae. The "I" bears four similarly mounted rubies, the "H" nine (one cabochon cut), the "S" six; to left and right, two small pearls. The scroll and framework connecting the initials are enameled opaque white, black, light and dark blue, and translucent green and red. At the bottom, the translucent red enameled heart, surmounted by three opaque black nails, bears a table-cut and collet-mounted diamond. From the bottom hang two pendant pearls. The reverse is brightly enameled in opaque black, white, light green, yellow and blue, and translucent red and green, with the instruments of the Passion: whip, crown of thorns, dice, bag of silver with "30" underneath, rods, hammer, pincers, column with cock, ladder and palm.

Height 2\/16 (5.2)
Width 1¼ (3.1)
Collection
    Emil Weinberger, Vienna
Exhibited
    Art Institute of Chicago (1951–1962) RX200/4
Published
    Weinberger Sale (1929)
BMA L.62.15.117
Gutman 1042

60

The question of provenance of this interesting jewel offers intriguing alternatives. To begin with it has been listed by Dr. Ernst Kris, who catalogued this piece in the Weinberger catalogue, as "South German (Salzburg?), about 1600," an attribution accepted by the Art Institute of Chicago. Nevertheless, and quite evidently, the coloring of the enamel points toward Spain, for it is correlative to that of the instruments of the Passion in no. 13, certainly a Spanish work, and the Guzmán Cross, formerly in the Morgan Collection (Williamson [1910] no. 58, pl. 24).

Moreover the two-dimensional, silhouetted composition is faithful to Spanish jewels of a class (cf. Johnson [1962] nos. 4, 6, 7, 9, 19 and 21; and Evans [1953] pl. VI and pl. 101; also Johnson [1944] figs. 90 and 91) which Johnson perspicaciously sees as "reminiscent of the mosaic tiles (*aliceres*) of Arabic inspiration" (1944, p. 117). Conversely, jewels of this class, with their planate and silhouetted character noted before are not at all comparable to the three-dimensional projection of South German-Austrian jewelry. At the same time, the possibility of an Elizabethan or Jacobean English date and provenance should not be slighted. Ross (1941) has demonstrated the connection between Spanish enamelers and those working in Surry in the early 17th century; the same planar, silhouetted outline may be seen in Jacobean jewels of about 1610 (Evans [1953] pl. 93c and the lid on pl. 94).

15   Pendant of the Paschal Lamb in Gold, Enamel and Jewels

SPANISH   CA. 1580–1600

The figure is suspended from a two-lobed cartouche enameled in opaque white and black, and translucent red, with a lozenge mount of four table-cut rubies and a suspended pearl. Two chains, each interrupted by a square-mounted, rectangular table-cut emerald flanked by four pearls, are attached by fixed rings to the head and hind quarters of the lamb. The figure, facing left, is of heavy opaque white enamel applied to a cast and carved gold base. The locks of fleece are enamel curls applied to roughly carved bases of similar shape. Attached across the front are three square-jeweled mounts bearing respectively, from left to right, four table-cut emeralds, four table-cut rubies and four table-cut emeralds. From the breast of the lamb emerges a coiled, flat spout of blood in gold which falls into a gold chalice with an eight-lobed base and hexagonal knop. The right forefoot of the lamb is raised and embraces a slender gold Cross, with arms surmounted by three pearls, which is bolted to the back. A glory stands in front of the base ring of the shorter left chain. From the lamb's belly is suspended a single pearl. Hooves and muzzle emerge as solid gold from the enamel. Parts of the black enamel of the lamb's right (back) eye are missing.

Height with chains and cartouche 2¹³⁄₁₆ (7.2)
Height of figure 1¾ (4.2)
Width 1¹⁵⁄₁₆ (4.9)
Collection
    Millicent Rogers
BMA L.62.15.1
Gutman unnumbered

For comparison with this excellently preserved jewel we find an almost identical example in the Victoria and Albert Museum (acc. no. M.456–1936, from the collection of Countess Harley Teleki), there somewhat arbitrarily called Hungarian, early 17th century, on the ground that it came from a Hungarian collection. However, the Spanish predilection for animal pendants, seen in the images from the Treasury of the Virgin of the Pillar, Saragossa (Evans [1953] p. 121) as well as other cathedrals (*viz.*, Palm, 1951) of Spanish affiliation, suggest rather that the pendant may be of Peninsular origin. It may be a confraternity badge of the late 16th century.

Likewise, the cartouche from which the lamb is suspended, ostensibly part of the original composition, is comparable to the usual type of this period (cf., no. 49 in this catalogue as well as Gutman Collection nos. 1153, 1202 and 1436).

16   Reliquary Pendant of Rock Crystal, Gold, Enamel and Wood

SPANISH   CA. 1590

A rectangular rock crystal case fits into a gold plinth with two columns on either side. The plinth is enameled in opaque black and white with scrolls and foliations. The two columns, with a spiral lower half enameled opaque blue and upper baluster enameled opaque black and white, pierce two flanges in the truncated pedimental roof and are topped by single pearls. The roof is enameled opaque black and white in a foliate pattern similar to the base, with minute dots of translucent green enamel, and is topped by a knopped ring enameled opaque white, with four droplets of translucent green. The interior wood-carving presents a Deposition and a Resurrection. The wood appears to be cedar.

Height 1¹¹⁄₁₆ (4.3)
Width 1⅛ (2.9)
Exhibited
    Art Institute of Chicago (1951–1962) RX200/42
BMA L.62.15.111
Gutman 1018

    This strongly constructed and boldly enameled piece bears the French owl import stamp after 1893. A very similar piece is in The Walters Art Gallery (acc. no. 61.120), and another, square, with four columns, is in the British Museum, Waddesdon Bequest (1902, p. 86, no. 182). The latter, in the cataloguer's opinion erroneously assigned to Germany, is dated 1591. The Walters reliquary is identified as Spanish, 16th century, and the Art Institute of Chicago accepts Mr. Gutman's identification of the present piece as Spanish, ca. 1600. There is no reason to take exception to this provenance, and, in view of the date on the Waddesdon piece, a date of ca. 1590 is proposed.

17 Pendant of Gold, Enamel, Rock Crystal, Pearl and Enclosed *Noli Me Tangere*

SOUTH (?) GERMAN   LATE 16TH CENTURY

Two elliptical rock crystal faces are held by a gold frame consisting of a central cylindrical band of opaque black and blue, and translucent green enamel between scalloped and punctured flanges. The frame opens on a simple pin hinge, to disclose Christ and Mary on either side of a tree. Mary at the left has opaque white enamel arms and face, a gold gown and translucent blue enamel mantle. The tree is enameled translucent green. Christ's robe is translucent red enamel and He rests His left hand upon a spade with an opaque blue enamel blade. Surrounding the tree and festooned from the top is a gold banner with the black enamel inscription: NOLI+ME+TANGERE+IOANZO.

Height 2¼ (5.8)
Width 1¹⁄₁₆ (2.7)
Exhibited
  Walters Art Gallery (1948)
  Detroit Institute of Arts (1958–1959) no. 359
Published
  Detroit (1958) no. 359
BMA L.62.15.11
Gutman 636

This crystal enclosed jewel, while patently representing a well-known New Testament subject, provides in the puzzling inscription "IOANZO" as neat an example as could be desired of the tyranny of preconception. Assuming that the piece was Italian, experts have always taken the word *Ioanzo* to be a superlative: "IO" ("I") + a dialectical and intruded form of "ANZI" ("Nay," "on the contrary"), i.e., "Touch me not, 'especially not now'." Dr. Edgar Breitenbach of the Library of Congress provided the witheringly simple solution: it is *Ioan(nes) 20* (Verse 17): "Touch me not; for I am not yet ascended to my Father." The provenance thus shifts to (probably South) Germany. A reasonable dating is that proposed by the owner and accepted by the Detroit Institute of Arts, late 16th century.

18 Pendant Double-Faced Cameo in Gold, Enamel and Coral: Christ and the Virgin

SICILIAN   EARLY 17TH CENTURY

The frame is suspended from a single opaque black enamel swivel-socket ring. The outer frame, executed in white opaque enamel and gold, consists of a bizarre open-work central bolster of contiguous diamond shapes punctured by circles over a continuous interior coral cylinder. This is attached by clamps top, bottom, left and right to an interior frame of opaque black enamel surrounding the cameo on both sides as a kind of shadow box. Obverse: nimbed Christ (nose damaged). Reverse: Madonna. Both figures bust length.

Height 1⅞ (4.7)
Width 1 (2.5)
Collections
   Prof. Luigi Grassi
   Henry Walters
Exhibited
   Walters Art Gallery (1948)
Published
   Grassi Sale (1927) no. 450, p. 170
   Walters Sale (1941) no. 1104, p. 326
BMA L.62.15.61
Gutman 585

66

This strongly shaped piece has been identified by Toesca as "very probably a South Italian or Sicilian votive jewel" (Grassi Sale [1927] no. 450, p. 170). Because of the prominent use of coral, however, a specialty of the craftsmen of Trapani, Sicily seems the more likely provenance of the two.

19   Locket of Gold and Enamel with Two Cameos: Christ and the Virgin

DUTCH AND NORTH ITALIAN   LATE 16TH AND EARLY 17TH CENTURIES

The frame is suspended from a single ring enameled opaque white with blue beads, painted black arabesques and two leaves of translucent green and yellow. The outer frame consists of a convex bolster divided into equal halves between beveled gold-hatched collars which hold the cameos. Foliate and floral designs of opaque blue and white, and translucent blue, green and yellow enamel with painted black dots cover the whole. The inner frame has yellow, blue, green, orange and black painted enamel flowers and leaves on opaque white. The cameo of the obverse is a bust of the Virgin, mantled, facing right. That of the reverse is an unnimbed bust of Christ facing left. The stone is a dark, translucent, striated brownish-red sard; the cameo of the Virgin contains many small suspended flecks throughout. Both cameos have been cut with smooth concave interiors.

Height 2⅝ (6.7)
Width 1¾ (4.5)
BMA L.62.15.60
Gutman 1385

The collars surrounding this forthright pair of cameos are in pristine condition, indicating that both frame and cameos have remained conjoint since their first assembly. Mr. Gutman is inclined to attribute the frame to Hans (Johan) Vermeyen (Vermayen, Vermeiden), the Brussels goldsmith who worked in Frankfurt-am-Main, settled in Vienna in 1597, and was named "Kammergoldschmied" by Rudolph II, and the cameos to one of the later Miseroni.

The cataloguer feels that an alternate suggestion is called for.

The cameos are of late 16th century Italian origin (cf., Eugen Gutman Collection, von Falke [1912] no. 98, pl. 19 and also our no. 12), and the frame, because of its simplicity of design and cheerful color, is more acceptably to be called Dutch of the early 17th century, for its restraint does not accord with the court style of Vermeyen, as exemplified by the frame surrounding a cameo by Jacopo da Trezzo (?) in the Kunsthistorisches Museum, Vienna (Steingräber [1956] no. 183).

68

20 Pendant Triptych of Gold, Lapis Lazuli, Rubies, Pearls and Two Miniatures

SPANISH (?)   EARLY 17TH CENTURY

The semicircular top of the frame rises from two colonnettes placed upon a gold plinth decorated with seven table-cut, collet-mounted rubies. The folding doors of polished lapis lazuli are fastened by a vertical sliding bolt in front, and are framed with a black enamel lozenge pattern separated by bars. The archivolt bears nine collet-mounted, table-cut rubies, the center one of which provides the socket for the bolt of the right hand door. The doors, on pin hinges within the colonnettes, open to disclose a miniature of the Virgin and Child within an inner black enameled border of gold circles and bars. The black enameled baluster ring is flanked by black enamel scrolls. The reverse is punch-tooled and carved, and enameled with the same lozenge and bar pattern; it contains a miniature of St. Joseph and the ass, while the plinth bears quatrefoils separated by bars. From black enamel scroll-work at the bottom depend three pearls, those to left and right in silver cup mounts; the center, oval pearl is baroque and pin fastened.

Height 2⁷⁄₁₆ (6.2)
Width closed 1 (2.5)
Width open 1¹⁵⁄₁₆ (4.6)
Collection
    Emil Weinberger (?)
Exhibited
    Art Institute of Chicago (1951–1962) RX200/50
BMA L.62.15.118
Gutman 1043

69

The documentation of the Art Institute of Chicago lists this piece as coming from the collection of Emil Weinberger although it did not appear in the Weinberger catalogue of 1929. Both Mr. Gutman and the Art Institute of Chicago regard the work as questionably South German, of the 16th century, and their uncertainty seems perfectly justified in the light of comparisons with other Gutman pieces, such as no. 16, Spanish, late 16th century. The miniatures are probably an intrusion substituting for a relic, a woodcarving (cf., no. 16) or an enameled devotional image.

Bloodstone Intaglio Pendant of Adam and Eve

GERMAN (?)　　MID-OR LATE 16TH CENTURY

This bloodstone intaglio of Adam and Eve is gouge carved and wheel cut. Adam, nude to left, covers himself with a branch held in the left hand and extends his right arm to Eve who, nude to right, extends her right hand to him and reaches into the tree above with her left. Between the two figures a trunk of a tree with foliage and apples above. Coiled in the fork of the tree at shoulder height the serpent extends an apple in his jaws. The simple frame with crimped edge appears to be gold-copper alloy.

Height 2⅛ (5.3)
Width 1⁹⁄₁₆ (4)
Exhibited
　　Walters Art Gallery (1948)
　　Art Institute of Chicago (1951–1962) RX200/11
BMA L.62.15.81
Gutman 770

This characteristically stylish pendant bears unmistakably the mannerisms of German figure drawing which relate to engravings from the second quarter of the 16th century by such German masters as Aldegrever and Hans Brosamer (cf., Hollstein, German I, B. 9 with Adam; and Hollstein, German IV, I, Pass. 23, with Eve). The very simple frame is appropriate but not localizable nor to be dated, but may well be coeval with the intaglio.

72

22 Heart-Shaped Pendant of Gold, Enamel and Rock Crystal with Eve and the Serpent

SPANISH (?) ITALIAN (?)   EARLY 17TH CENTURY

The pendant is heart shaped but asymmetrical, the right side being slightly concave at the bottom. Two polished rock crystal faces are held by a wide basic band between two corded borders. Attached to this is the elaborately wrought and enameled stem: a pineapple on a leaved stalk enameled translucent green and red. Around the band meanders a wrought vine with tendrils, leaves, flowers and fruit enameled translucent green, reddish brown, blue, red and opaque white. Between the two faces is seen, to left, the serpent coiled around a tree and, to right, Eve seated, with foliage behind. All figures are modeled *en ronde bosse*. The serpent's body is striped with translucent red, green and black enamel. The trunk of the tree and leaves are the same brown and green enamel of the exterior stem and leaves, and so are the foliage and the rock upon which Eve sits. Flesh parts are opaque white with a greenish mottling. The hair of both the serpent and Eve was originally the same brown as the tree trunk, but it has subsequently been gilded, as have the eyelids, eyes, lips and chins in both figures. Eve's right hand holding the apple has been repaired, and there is evidence of repair on the right side of her face and neck, and on the left side of the serpent's face and nose. The back of the stem has also been repaired and resoldered. There is a crack $^{15}\!/_{16}$ inches long in the front face.

Height 2$^{15}\!/_{16}$ (7.4)
Width 1$^{11}\!/_{16}$ (4.3)
BMA L.62.15.204
Gutman 1320

While it is perhaps all too fallible to suggest a provenance for this eye-catching piece on the grounds of shape alone, nonetheless several comparable rock crystal hearts of Spanish origin must be cited (Johnson [1962] no. 14; Desmoni Sale [1960] nos. 27 and 28), together with another jeweled heart (Desmoni Sale, no. 76), all conforming to the same asymmetrical shape. There are other heart shaped brooches, and also the heart shaped Lennox (or Darnley) Jewel; but these, in contrast to the present jewel, are symmetrical (Evans [1921] p. 45; [1953] pp. 105 and 126).

According to Dr. Carl Swanson of the Biology Department at The Johns Hopkins University, the occurence of the pineapple was primarily associated with the Spanish and Portuguese colonies, partly because it was on the Caribbean island of Guadeloupe that Christopher Columbus first received the pineapple from the Indians. It was only in the late 16th and 17th centuries that the pineapple became so esteemed as "an occasional delicacy in Europe that the nobility of 17th and 18th century England and France set their gardeners and greenhouses to the task of supplying it." (Schery [1952] p. 480.) This would seem to point to Spain (or Portugal?) rather than Italy, but not France or England where the first reference to the *ananas sativus* is in the diary of John Evelyn in the mid-17th century.

No connection between any of these jewels and the late 17th century cult of the Sacred Heart of Marguerite Marie Alacoque should be inferred.

73

23   Circular Pendant in Silver Gilt and Niello with the Virgin as *Regina Coeli* and the Mass of St. Gregory

SOUTH GERMAN   CA. 1500

The frame is suspended by a single ring at the top from a single beaded silver loop. The circular niello plaque is enclosed by a spiral cord alternating with a convex plain band and beading. This is soldered to the two-part inner frame, which consists on each side of a row of beads and a plain bevelled edge. The outside cord masks the join of the two frames between which the plaque is held. On the front, the Virgin as *Regina Coeli* holds the Christ Child in her arms. Her heavily draped figure stands within the crescent moon, and is surrounded by an aureole of twenty-three alternately straight and wavy rays. Two nude winged putti hold a crown over her head. There is an internal border of a heart-shaped pattern with points facing outward. On the back, the Mass of St. Gregory; the robed saint kneels, facing left, before the altar, above which the vision appears; bystanders to right and left. The surface is much worn, and the filling deteriorated; individual details have almost disappeared.

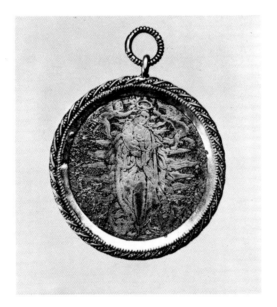 

Height from loop 2⅛ (5.4)
Width 1⅞ (4.8)
Collections
   Robert Forrer, Strassburg
   Kunsthaus, Zürich
Exhibited
   Hohenlohe-Kunstgewerbemuseum, Strassburg (1904)
Published
   Forrer (1905) p. 18, ill. p. 20, fig. 117
   von Falke (1928) p. 38, no. 44, ill. p. 15
BMA L.62.15.47
Gutman 1300

This intact pendant is interestingly related to other arts of its day and has been the subject of previous research. Forrer (1905) attributes it to German workmanship and the 15th century; von Falke (1928) agrees with the date but makes the piece Italian; the cataloguer is inclined to agree with Forrer. Both in technique and iconography the Virgin and the Mass of St. Gregory are consistent with the carved (woodcut) approach used in silver, and to imagery of the years between 1480 and 1510.

Compare, for example, the drapery and alternating straight and wavy rays of the aureole with the woodcut in the Cabinet des Estampes (Lemoisne [1930] pl. CVII) of between 1480 and 1500, and the Mass of St. Gregory in Burgkmair's illustration for the *Taschenbüchlein aus einem Closter in dem Ries*, Augsburg, 1510 (Hollstein, German V, pp. 70–71).

A very similar frame, surrounding a mother-of-pearl depiction of the Adoration of the Magi, is in the Victoria and Albert Museum (acc. no. 39. 1894, Inventory of Art Objects [1894] p. 8, "German, Early 15th century") now assigned to Germany, 15th century. The harmoniously joined frame and plaque are coeval.

24 Pendant of Gold, Enamel, Baroque Pearl and Emeralds: St. Jerome

SPANISH   LATE 16TH AND EARLY 18TH CENTURIES

The pendant is suspended by two chains, of equal length and identical design, from the two table-cut emeralds which flank a central square, table-cut emerald mounted in a high conical collet, the base of which is surrounded by beading. The three stones are connected at the top by two gold volutes; a single pin-fastened pearl depends from the central emerald. Each chain consists of two plain links and a central link of an elliptical beaded collet containing a rectangular table-cut emerald. All these mounts are fully backed. The collets, including the beading, are separate, integral pieces which have been pressed down over the stones and soldered at the edges to the backing. The pendant proper consists of three distinct parts. The first is a hollow, ovoid, straight-walled gold casing surrounded by a carved, open-work border of foliations and guilloches, with twelve conically mounted square and rectangular table-cut emeralds of varying sizes, the mounts repeating, in four instances, the beaded base of the chains and suspender. From openwork volutes on either side depend two pin-fastened pearls with pleated biconical collars. The second part is a frame, fitting snugly into the central cavity, masking its plain face with a second face of four flattened volutes with traces of opaque white and red enamel. This portion is removable. The third part consists of a baroque pearl utilized as the landscape setting for a figure of St. Jerome, left, cast and carved, with traces of translucent red enamel, before a Crucifix, right, with his hat (?), also enameled translucent red, attached to the back wall. On the reverse, the backs of the chain, the surrounding border and case are engraved with foliate sprays and rosettes, over a mat finish, and the monogram VM.

Height 2³⁄₁₆ (5.6)
Width 1⁵⁄₈ (4.1)
Collections
   Luigi Grassi
   Henry Walters
Exhibited
   Walters Art Gallery (1948)
   Detroit Institute of Arts (1958–1959)
Published
   Grassi Sale (1927) no. 480
   Walters Sale (1943) no. 988, ill. p. 185
   Detroit (1958) no. 358, ill. p. 149
BMA L.62.15.165
Gutman 895

In the catalogues of the Grassi Sale, the Walters Sale and the Detroit Institute of Arts, the piece is called "Italian, end of the 16th century" with the proviso that "the setting of the emeralds and the

entire shape of the pendant clearly denote Spanish influence on Italian art at the end of the 16th century."
There is no need, however, for such an indirection, for the pendant is entirely Spanish.

The conical beaded mounts enclosing table-cut stones are a continuing Spanish device (cf., Johnson [1944] figs. 98, 112, 221 and 222). Also there is a similar pendant in the collection of the Hispanic Society of America (Johnson [1962] no. 22, "First half of the 17th century") and another in the Victoria and Albert Museum (acc. no. 321–1870, Inventory of Art Objects [1870] p. 30) from the Treasury of the Virgin of the Pillar, Saragossa, with the Adoration of the Magi in enameled gold under crystal, Spanish, late 17th century.

The Gutman pendant, because of the distinctively early rococo character of the engraving, should be dated in the early 18th century. This does not preclude, however, the possibility of the center jewel itself being of earlier date, indeed of the second half of the 16th century, a handsome nugget in its own right.

25 Pelican Pendant Whistle with Gold, Enamel, Rubies and Baroque Pearls

SPANISH (?)   CA. 1600   *Color plate facing page 42*

The body of the pelican in this pendant whistle consists of a large, roughly bifurcated baroque pearl. To this are attached the various cast, carved and enameled parts of the bird. The neck and head, which bend forward over the breast, are hollow cast and enameled opaque white, black (eyes) and translucent red (tongue). In the forehead is fastened a square, collet-mounted table-cut ruby. The open wings are attached through the pearl by heavy gold wires and an added bolt. Each wing bears a separate mount of three rectangular, table-cut rubies; the enamel is opaque white. The hollow cast legs fit over the two nether protrusions of the pearl and are held in place by long bolts running through them vertically and fastened on the underside of the whistle; the legs are enameled opaque white and black. The hollow cast tail is fitted onto the pearl between the legs and held in place by a single bolts (silver, new) in back. The bird's talons grasp a hollow cast gold log, the whistle, from which depends a single pearl. Soldered to this, between the legs of the pelican and in front of the tail, is a concave gold disc holding the hollow, cast and carved gold representation of a nest containing three fledglings; one of which has been attacked and bitten in back by a snake whose head is seen beneath the breasts of the two unharmed fledglings. The birds are enameled opaque white and black, the serpent is opaque green, the nest opaque blue. Five circular holes penetrate the nest between and in front of the birds. The bore of each hole is rifled as though, perhaps, to contain pearls or jewels screwed into position. The nest and figures are held within the disc by a single bolt.

Height including pearl drop 2¹⁵⁄₁₆ (7.5)
Width 2⅛ (5.4)
Collection
    Anonymous French family
Exhibited
    Walters Art Gallery (1948)
    Art Institute of Chicago (1951–1962) RX200/18
Published
    D'Otrange (1952) p. 70, ill. pp. 67 and 69
    Hackenbroch (1954) pp. 168–172, ill. pl. 94, no. E
    Stone (1958) pp. 196 and 198, ill. p. 195
BMA L.62.15.88
Gutman 905

The uniqueness of this pendant resides not only in its several peculiarities, for it is at once a striking object of costume, a serviceable whistle and an object of religious connotation: the so-called Pelican-in-its-Piety, but it is also a work of singular beauty and blunt vigor by a superior craftsman. Its provenance has been thought to be French, for it was acquired from "an old French family." Nevertheless, the greater possibility that it is of Spanish origin must be put forward. First should be mentioned the prevalence of animalistic pendants among the votive offerings deposited before the Saragossa Virgen del Pilar (cf., Evans [1953] p. 121, pl. 76 and Smith [1909] p. 249, pl. XXXIV, nos. 1 and 2).

Moreover, the regular disposition of jewels over the body of such pieces is a Spanish predilection (cf., Mr. Gutman's objects nos. 1153, 1207 and 1436) and the free-standing figure in general seems to be a Spanish preference. In contrast, two pelican pendants recently sold at Sotheby's (Dec. 5, 1960, nos. 114 and 117) surrounded by intricate architectural frameworks "in the manner of Hans Collaert," and manifesting a totally different approach to this subject, are German. A French attribution, though it cannot be ruled out, is rendered less likely also by the extreme paucity of French Renaissance jewelry, owing to the attrition of wars and revolutions.

26   Pendant of Gold, Enamel and Amethyst

SPANISH   17TH CENTURY

The frame is suspended from a cast and carved baluster ring ending in two volutes and enameled opaque white. The gold outer wall is cast and carved and nine six-leaved rosettes, enameled opaque white, separate the Instruments of the Passion, which are gold with an opaque black ground. This outer wall has soldered to it a border of twenty-eight tiny circular collets originally containing droplets of opaque white enamel giving the effect of seed pearls. Fitting into this outer frame is a second frame, also cordered with circular collets, which holds in place an oval, flattened, cabochon-cut amethyst. Fitting over the amethyst are two oval hoops, the first contains a Crucifixion, with *titulus* enameled opaque black and the Cincture and Crown of Thorns enameled opaque white. The Crucifixion is held firmly in place by the amethyst behind and by the two arms and foot of the cross which fit into notches in the border of circles on the face. The second hoop, on the reverse, contains the Virgin as Queen of Heaven enameled opaque blue and white with red and yellow mottling. This is held in place by the second frame, which fits snugly into the outer housing.

Height 1½ (3.7)
Width ¾ (2)
Collection
    Edward J. Berwind, New York
Exhibited
    Walters Art Gallery (1948)
Published
    Berwind Sale (1939) no. 362
    D'Otrange (1953) ill. p. 133
BMA L.62.15.172
Gutman 555

A clerical error evidently led D'Otrange to publish this piece as "French, 16th Century." This piece was no. 362 of the Berwind Sale, an "Enameled Gold Locket, Spanish, XVI–XVII Century." The pendant is a more aristocratic version of the typical early 17th century Spanish *Capillita de santero* (Galter [1948] pl. 460). The amethyst, which, because of its conformity to the frame must be considered original, came into Spanish fashion again at this period, first, because of its relative cheapness as against the ruby and balas, and second, because of its somber, sanguinary color congenial with the religiosity of the age. The ease with which the stone can be removed leads to the surmise that several different replacements might have been used for symbolic, therapeutic or magical purposes, as birthstones, panaceas or amulets.

27 Rosary of Seven Boxwood Skulls and Crescent Shaped Pendant

CENTRAL EUROPEAN   16TH CENTURY

The chain is composed of a ring, eight metal links, seven wooden links and a pendant. The silver gilt ring has a center row of a double-corded band between two single-corded bands all soldered to the outside of a circular hoop. From this depends a boss and loop surrounded by a spiral collar; the chain proper is suspended from this ring. The metal links consist of buoy shaped, *ajouré,* eight-corded arches, on either side of a central band of translucent green enamel, the upright of each arch being decorated with an opaque white enamel bead. The wooden links consist of carved boxwood skulls which are fastened by simple hook and eye fasteners with link hinges. Each skull opens in back to reveal two tiny carved wooden scenes in relief within an oval frame set against an iridescent background of peacock or similar feathers. From ring to crescent the scenes are as follows:

Skull 1 left —The Visitation
right—Christ Among the Doctors(?)
Skull 2 left   —Flight Into Egypt
right—Adoration of the Magi
Skull 3 left   —St. Jerome
right—St. Anthony of Padua
Skull 4 left   —Mary and Joseph Adoring the Child (?)
right—The Annunciation
Skull 5 left   —Flagellation
right—The Beating With Rods (?)
Skull 6 left   —Christ On The Mount Of Olives
right—*Pietà*
Skull 7 left   —Doubting Thomas
right—Washing of the Feet

The boxwood edge surrounding each carving shows traces of gilding. From the eighth metal link is suspended a crescent shaped, silver-gilt and niello pendant with corded borders and spiral collars at the top and ends of the crescent and center lobe, two plaques of very crude workmanship, with inlay only fragmentary. On one side, the Virgin as seated Queen of Heaven between the winged heads of two angels, and on the other side the crowned and robed Christ holding the cross in His left hand between the heads of two winged angels. From the center lobe there is suspended a small silver gilt *crux ansata* and from the ends of the crescent two hollow segmented beads of which only one is intact.

Length 15¼ (38.7)
Width with skull closed 13⁄16 (2)
Width with skull opened 1 (2.5)
Height of pendant and loop 2⅛ (5.4)
Width of pendant 1 5⁄16 (3.3)
Exhibited
   Art Institute of Chicago (1951–1962) RX200/51
BMA L.62.15.119
Gutman 1047

A technically skillful performance lends this piece added interest. Seven of the normal ten parts are preserved here, evidently from a Central European tradition, although the terminal pendant, less elegant, by shape and workmanship appears to be from another more Eastern source. The scenes within the skulls, having been separately made and inserted, may account for the iconographic displacement which, for example, puts Christ Among the Doctors in the first skull with The Visitation. There are few clues to exact provenance except possibly in the images of Saints Jerome and Anthony of Padua (a Franciscan); the significance of their presence here, however, is not ostensible.

28 Boxwood Noix, Diptych, with Two Scenes from the Life of Christ

GERMAN (?)   15TH CENTURY

The sphere, fastened on one side by a simple pin hinge and on the other by an identical pin bolt with chain, divides into two equal hemispheres, each carved in a flamboyant Gothic whorl of twenty-four parts. The poles are capped by silver rosettes with attached loops. Two beaded borders surround the equator, each half discloses on the interior two finely carved scenes, the Expulsion of the Money Changers and the Entry into Jerusalem. These have been carved into separate hemispheres inserted in the exterior cage through which the reddish painted surface can be seen.

Height with loops 1¹⁵⁄₁₆ (4.6)
Width with hinges 1⁹⁄₁₆ (3.9)
Collections
    Jules S. Bache, New York
    Joseph Brummer
Exhibited
    Art Institute of Chicago (1951–1962) RX200/56
Published
    Bache Sale (1945) p. 116, no. 459, ill. p. 117
    Brummer Sale (1949) I, no. 635
BMA L.62.15.124
Gutman 1073

All previous attributions have agreed on a German Rhenish provenance, although they vary as to dating. However, there are no really plausible grounds for certainty. The fluid, attenuated flamboyant motifs of the exterior are compatible with widespread examples from the 15th century. The clean-cut separation and three-dimensionality of the interior carving differ from the rampant intricacy of natural detail so often seen in German sculpture of the same period.

One may compare, for example, a prayer nut associated with Flanders about 1500 (cf. Thoma and Hege [1955] fig. 22) and a miniature tabernacle in the Waddesdon Bequest identified as "Flemish, early 16th century." In this last, the forms are more ornate, somewhat more lavish in tracery and foliage, and perhaps, therefore, later than our example, the probable date of which can be limited to about 1480–1500; the origin should be broadened to include Flanders, and perhaps France, as well as the German Rhineland.

Large Boxwood Noix, Triptych with Scenes from the
Biblia Pauperum

SOUTH NETHERLANDISH   CA. 1500–1510

The case is an oblate sphere carved front and back with a thirteen-pointed rose of overlapping ogives forming a network of irregular lozenges, each lozenge containing an open quatrefoil. The center is a circle containing three circles with quatrefoils. The equator consists of two flat borders, each with a zigzag carving on either side of a raised, interlaced vine in the form of a guilloche. The front, bolted through three mortises, opens into two equal halves to form a triptych. The carving on the jambs of the doors is slightly recessed: above, a pinwheel rosette; below, a pilgrim's pouch hanging on a peg. The carving of the interior faces of the doors is disposed as follows. *Left door:* above, two angels face to face holding a crown between them; center, eight kneeling ecclesiastical and secular figures in two registers; below, two music making angels face to face, the left with a harp, the right with a psaltery. *Right door:* above, two angels face to face holding a crown between them; center, six kneeling figures preceded by two bishops, eight in all; below, two music-making angels, both with recorders. The back planes of both doors and their jambs are ornamented with random rosettes, each consisting of five or six punch marks in a polygon with one punch at the center. *Central roundel:* bottom, Adoration of the Child, with the Virgin left, Joseph right, Child center, ox and ass in background, in front of and beneath a dormered and partially destroyed roof; to left, two peasants leaning upon a gate; to right, two peasants, hands clasped, dance to a bagpipe played by a turbaned peasant behind. Center field, left, a kneeling figure surrounded by sheep in a rocky landscape, with scroll bearing angel above; center, above the manger roof, Moses on Mount Horeb before the Burning Bush (*Exodus* III, 2); right, Gideon, as a knight in full armor, kneeling in prayer before the Fleece (*Judges* VI, 37–40); in center background, the Flowering of Aaron's Rod among the Twelve in the Tabernacle (*Numbers*

XVII). Around the scenes themselves is a Latin inscription, with many abbreviations, from the Vulgate, *Matthew* II, 6: "Et tu, Bethlehem, terra Iuda, nequaquam minima es in principilbus Iuda; ex te enim exiet dux qui regat populum meum Israel." On the left door is the word *martelaere*; on the right door, *ofessorn*.

Height from stationary loop 2¹¹⁄₁₆ (6.7)
Width 2⁵⁄₁₆ (5.8)
Collection
   Baron von Dorn, Kassel
BMA L.62.15.178
Gutman unnumbered

The spelling of *martelaere* on the left door leaves no doubt of the Netherlandish origin of this piece, as pointed out (*in litteris*) by Jaap Leeuwenberg, Curator of Sculptures at the Rijksmuseum. The scenes in the central roundel are in part a conflation from the *Biblia Pauperum* (cf. Munich, Staatsbibliothek, Clm. 8201, fol. 81r in Cornell [1925] pl. 28) in respect to the ordinance of the Nativity, Moses and the Burning Bush, Gideon and the Fleece, and the Flowering of Aaron's Rod. The fine carving, probably derived from engraved or woodcut forebears, may be later than the date of its sources, which display in the peasants' unwieldy, orientalized headgear and Gideon's armor the modes of about 1500–1515 (cf. Waetzoldt [1950] figs. 125, 132, 133).

30 Pendant of Gold, Enamel and Jewels with St. George (?), Charity (?), Pelican and Dragon

SOUTH GERMAN (WITH ADDITIONS)   CA. 1600   *Color plate facing page 168*

The pendant consists of four distinct parts. Part One is a roughly lozenge-shaped, cast, carved and enameled basic structure suspended from a single fixed ring. At the top, surmounting a crown, is a Pelican-in-her-Piety, the body enameled opaque blue, the feathers of the outstretched wings enameled alternately opaque white and translucent red; three fledglings enameled opaque light blue; and, between the pelican's outstretched feet, beneath and surrounding an oval opening (filled with Part Two), a composition of interlocked volutes and blossoms enameled opaque black, white, blue and green, and translucent red. The gold in this section of the frame has been punch-tooled with a small convex-tip punch. In the center of the crown, and to the left and right, three square, table-cut, collet-mounted diamonds in silver-gilt mounts are bolted to the back through holes in the frame. Across the widest part at the bottom is a recumbent monstrous figure with horned head, talons and wings, the body enameled opaque pale green and yellow, the head gray, and the wings translucent red, green and blue. Beneath this, also bolted through the frame, is a cabochon-cut emerald in a high collet mount of silver-gilt similar to the diamonds mentioned above. From a link at the bottom, suspended also in a silver-gilt collet mount open in back, is a marquise-cut diamond. The back of this part of the frame continues two-dimensionally: the pelican, crown, volutes, scrolls and flowers with blossoms are enameled opaque white, blue, lavender, green and black, and translucent red and blue. Portions have been punch-tooled to a mat finish with a cylindrical punch. The carving has not been finished off, which gives a somewhat cruder aspect than that of the obverse. Part Two consists of a cast, carved and enameled oval gold framework which overlays Part One and fits into the oval, open, central space of the basic frame. It

89

is a composition of flowers and volutes enameled opaque blue, lavender, black, white and yellow. A punch-tooled central square of gold serves as the base for a cabochon-cut ruby in a collet mount of silver-gilt, rather roughly bolted to the back. Part Three comprises two figures, A and B, left and right respectively, mounted over Parts One and Two, and securing all together by means of the fastening bolts in their backs. Figure A, the male figure on the left, is an exquisitely worked knight in full parade armor, carved and punch-tooled in a guilloche pattern with margins and panels enameled opaque white, yellow and light blue. A Maltese Cross, enameled translucent red, is upon the breastplate. He holds a thin copper-gilt lance in his left hand and sits with the left knee drawn up and left foot in the crook of the right knee. Two pins soldered to the lower part of the figure in back penetrate through holes in Parts One and Two. Figure B, the female figure on the right, is dressed in an opaque blue enamel upper garment, with a lower skirt punch-tooled in the same manner as the man's armor, with a translucent red enamel lining. She holds two nude male children in both arms. The child on the left reaches his right hand to a translucent red enamel jewel at her breast. This figure is similarly fastened through Parts One and Two, and bolted at the back. Part Four is the hinged and latched back of Part Two. This is an uncarved lid of gold, with *champlevé* enamel scrolls and flowers in opaque black, white, yellow and blue above, beneath and on either side of a central composition of a heart surmounted by a crown with flames, flanked by two outstretched hands. The heart and flames bear traces of translucent red enamel. The crown is opaque blue. This fastens by a pin latch to Part One.

Height 2⁷⁄₁₆ (6.2)
Width 1¹¹⁄₁₆ (4.2)
BMA L.62.15.185
Gutman 1365

This sumptuous piece in all its parts gives an immediate effect of unity and coherence. However, it is clearly composite, for the frame (Part One) is stylistically consistent with late 16th century South German examples. Part Two appears to be an inserted piece, perhaps a substitution for a larger, semiprecious, translucent stone, such as an amethyst, while the silver-gilt mounts of the stones are incompatible with the fundamental workmanship, indicating that they, too, are additions. The two figures constituting Part Three, are superlatively worked. Dismounted, they are revealed as fully enameled and tooled from the waist up, leading to the conclusion that they were meant to be viewed at least half in the round, or through a more open, airier frame than that now provided. The tooling and enameling of both figures presupposes the same artisan. The hinged back (Part Four) of exceedingly delicate design, is apparently part of a betrothal locket (viz., the clasped hands) relating in style to the designs of Etienne Carteron (Evans [1953] fig. 19), the asymmetrical design of which would place this part of the work about 1600 (cf., *ibid.*, pl. 95).

Iconographically, while the Pelican-in-her-Piety at the top (The Church Triumphant) might be connected with the female figure of Charity (or Cornelia?) below, the monster at the bottom of the frame, which is overlaid and partially hidden by the two figures, has no connection with the iconographic scheme unless one understands the male in armor not as a Knight of Malta, but St. George, whose *dégagé* pose, however, hardly befits the Church Militant. Richard Randall of the Walters Art Gallery fixes the armor as of a Germanic type of the mid-16th century or later.

92

31 Pendant of Gold, Enamel and Jewels with Cimon and Pera

SOUTH GERMAN   CA. 1600–1610

The pendant consists of three cast, carved and tooled layers or tiers, bolted together to form a three-dimensional ensemble of great vigor and delicacy. The first layer, or base, is essentially a lozenge with two long and two short sides, composed of interlocking scrolls, volutes and swags emerging from a central vertical shaft. This layer is partially punch-tooled with both convex rounded point and cylindrical punches, and has been enameled opaque white and green, and translucent blue and red. Three pin-fastened pearls depend from rings at the bottom; two seed pearls are fastened to left and right at the top. Slightly beneath these are two silver-gilt rivets which may originally have fastened smaller mounted stones in pyramidal collets similar to those remaining. The second layer is a series of secondary tooled and enameled scrolls and volutes, bolted at three places through the central spine, and centered by, top, a triangular table-cut ruby in a high pyramidal collet mount enameled opaque white, and, to left and right, smaller rubies in similarly enameled mounts. At the bottom is a table-cut diamond with a collet mount enameled opaque black. The central bolt holds in place a spreading, punch-tooled pair of tendrils enameled translucent red and blue, each bearing a pyramidally mounted table-cut diamond with plain gold collets. Above this, held out from the first two layers by two gold cylinders, the third layer, the hollow cast, carved and tooled group of Cimon and Pera. Cimon, flesh parts enameled opaque white, sits chained upon a stone shelf, enameled translucent blue over rusticated carving, with a punch-tooled drapery about his loins. Pera sits to the left, clad in a translucent blue enamel mantle over a punch-tooled gold gown with a swirling drapery behind; she embraces her father with her left arm and exposes her left breast with her right arm. To the left is a carved ewer, enameled translucent blue. Between the legs of the figures, a triangular table-cut collet-mounted ruby.

Height 2⅞ (7.2)
Width 2¹⁄₁₆ (5.3)
Collections
    Mme. la Comtesse Livia Zichy
    Joseph Brummer
Published
    Pulszky, Radisics and Milinier (1884) II, pp. 20, 21
    Brummer Sale (1949) I, no. 670
    D'Otrange (1952) p. 32, no. XVIII
    Hackenbroch (1954) pl. 96
BMA L.62.15.184
Gutman 1065

The workmanship here is of a high order. There are, fortunately, other works of the same type and subject with which this may be compared. The first is a pendant in the Rijksmuseum, Amsterdam, formerly in the Eugen Gutman Collection (Steingräber [1956] fig. 204, given to Germany at the end of the 16th century), and given by von Falke (1912, no. 7) to South Germany, end of the 16th century. The

Rijksmuseum pendant is so close in configuration to a particular design by Collaert (Steingräber, fig. 203), that a date between 1581 and about 1600 is mandatory. Here the framework is more compact and the workmanship not so delicate as the Melvin Gutman example. The second is a pendant formerly in the Desmoni Collection (Desmoni Sale [1960] no. 119; the catalogue cites the Melvin Gutman pendant as a parallel), rather widely placed within the second half of the 16th century in Germany.

Stylistically, the cataloguer would place the Melvin Gutman pendant as the latest of the three, about 1600–1610. The concentrated architectural framework of Collaert has here become a more attenuated, visually penetrable scaffolding, such as is seen in the designs of Birckenhulz, 1617, and Mignot, 1616 (Evans [1953] figs. 16 and 17). The cataloguer has argued (*Introduction*, p. 29) that the engraved designs for jewelry cannot be infallibly accepted as *termini a quo*, since many may, indeed, have been inspired as exercises by jewels already extant. However, the fine Melvin Gutman pendant could be after the Collaert-Rijksmuseum type.

There are certain discrepancies in the construction of this piece which serve notice that it may be partially composite. In the central shaft, visible from both the back and front behind the head of Pera, is a circular gold plug, which, in back, is almost flush with the surrounding area and similarly gouge cut, as if meant to be covered by the now fragmentary translucent enamel. The plug has been cut off in front and cross-hatched to render it less conspicuous and may have been the original support, or rivet, for a different central composition.

The base of the Cimon and Pera group is enameled translucent blue with a gold arabesque pattern now obscured by the large mount of the bottom diamond; the decoration must originally have been meant to be seen in its entirety. The cylinder holding the central group out from the spine is in two parts, as if one part had been added to piece out the greater distance. If the central group had been part of the original design, a single cylinder would have been all that was needed, and the fine enameling of the base, now seen only when the jewel is upturned, would have been omitted. The collets of the gems, though pristine, are not consistent in pattern, and the bolts which hold them in place, as well as the bolt of the central group, are fastened over the original tooling. At the top, beneath the bolt of the ruby, is a silver splitpin holding in place the white enamel scroll beneath the ruby, which interferes with the composition of the surrounding tendrils. All these bolts would have made the reverse distinctly unsightly when new and brilliantly enameled.

This piece sets forth both the structural elements and their ornamentation at one striking view, which is characteristic of late mannerist craftsmanship, as in a gold and enamel pendant with a central figure of Venus with dolphins in the British Museum, Waddesdon Bequest (1902, p. 72, no. 150, ill. pl. XXXV). In this connection the annotated copy of the Waddesdon Bequest catalogue in the Department of British and Medieval Antiquities, British Museum, contains the superscription, "Dr. E. Kris says late 16th Century"); it is given now to Germany, 16th century, and has a frame and disposition of jewels much like the Melvin Gutman piece, but the collets of the jewels are an integral part of the basic design. Another pendant in the Victoria and Albert Museum (M. 387–1911, South Germany, about 1600) has the same technique of mounting pieces together with hollow cylinders (in this instance, single) and the same enamel droplets on the scrolls.

32 Pendant of Gold, Enamel, Baroque Pearls and Gems: Mars and Venus

NORTH ITALIAN   LATE 16TH CENTURY

The pendant is suspended from a baluster ring with opaque black central band, translucent green pellet and knop with opaque white droplets. This emerges from the top of one of four symmetrically placed banderoles enameled translucent red and green, which bind a cast and carved laurel wreath. Within the wreath a fillet frame with opaque white band encloses a bloodstone plaque of elliptical shape to which is attached the group of Mars and Venus. Mars, right, embraces Venus, left. Both figures are seated in a rocky landscape. Limbs and faces are enameled opaque white (there is extensive cold paste repair on the neck of Venus). The trunks of both figures are large baroque pearls, partially carved. Both figures are surrounded by an elaborate interplay of cast and carved gold drapery and both wear greaves on their visible left legs: that of Venus is enameled translucent red; of Mars, opaque white. The rocks bear traces of translucent green and yellow enamel. This part of the composition contains five cabochon-cut stones, two emeralds, two rubies and a sapphire, in fringed collet mounts. The back of the bloodstone plaque is masked by a flat silver surface evidently intended to be polished as a mirror. A single baroque pin-fastened pearl is suspended by a baluster mount from the bottom of the inclosing wreath.

Height 3⅝ (9.3)
Width 2 (5.1)
Collections
  Charles Stein
  Baron Max von Goldschmidt-Rothschild
Exhibited
  Art Institute of Chicago (1951–1962)
Published
  Stein Sale (1886) no. 155
  Goldschmidt-Rothschild Sale (1950) II, no. 99
  D'Otrange (1953) ill. p. 69
  Hackenbroch (1954) pl. 94c
BMA L.62.15.140
Gutman 1147

This is a piece of singularly happy proportions and balance between frame and figurative pendant. Charles Mannheim, in the Stein catalogue, calls this piece Italian, 16th century; the Goldschmidt-Rothschild Sale catalogue calls it South German, early 17th century; the Art Institute of Chicago, D'Otrange and Hackenbroch say South German or Italian, 16th century, which is agreed to by Mr. Gutman. The cataloguer resists the temptation to consolidate all these attributions into the attractive hamper of "South German or Italian, 16th-17th centuries" and suggests instead the more limited designation of North Italian, end of the 16th century, on particular and general stylistic grounds.

The particular grounds concern the frame which belongs to the archaeological and sculpturesque traditions to be found in the designs of such an artist as Enea Vico, of Parma (1523–1567) (Guilmard [1881] II, pl. 96) and, as a direct parallel, the frame of a wax portrait, North Italian, end of the 16th century, in the Metropolitan Museum of Art (Steingräber [1956] pl. 232). The group of Mars and Venus, on the other hand, is of mannerist persuasion in the vein of Collaert. It is not uninformative that the design of Enea Vico cited above combines, as does this piece, a severe base with a sinuous and entwined composition. The heliotrope backing may not be coeval and may further indicate a North Italian provenance (cf., nos. 12 and 19 in this catalogue).

Pendant of Gold, Enamel and Jewels with Baroque Pearl Bust

NORTH ITALIAN   LATE 16TH CENTURY

The pendant is suspended from an openwork cartouche of four opaque white enamel volutes on a circular frame of translucent blue enamel, with two curvilinear triangles or scallops, right and left, of translucent red. A pendant pearl occupies the circular space and a second pearl hangs from a ring at the bottom of the cartouche. There are two chains, each of four links: two links consist of capped pearls between rings, and two links are rings decorated with segments of opaque white and translucent red enamel. The pendant proper is an architectural niche, composed of an archivolt of six table-cut rubies in collet mounts, acting as voussoirs, with a triangular table-cut emerald as keystone. Opaque blue and white enamel concave scrolls break up the exterior profile. At the springings are two table-cut emeralds in collet mounts. Within the archivolt is an openwork fan of opaque blue enamel above a translucent red lintel. An opaque white enamel boss is suspended from beneath the keystone. This complex is supported by two free-standing black enamel columns standing upon plinths of collet-mounted, table-cut emeralds. Behind the columns, rusticated masonry of punch-tooled gold is indicated, and from semicircular flanges enameled translucent red, to right and left, spring trefoil flowerets of translucent blue, with three-pointed opaque green enamel leaves and long opaque white pistils. Two oval pearls hang from rings at the margins. Between the columns is the bust of a bearded male, facing left, hollow-cast and carved. The hair, beard and mustache are of gold, the flesh parts opaque white with opaque blue enamel eyes. The bare torso is a baroque pearl, surrounded by billowing drapery of translucent red and blue enamel. The bust rises from a tapering three-sided bracket enameled opaque blue, and centered by a table-cut, collet-mounted ruby. Beneath the emerald plinths is a symmetrical arrangement of scrolls and flowers, enameled opaque light blue and white, and translucent red and dark blue, with an hexagonal, fancy-cut sapphire in a collet mount in the center. A single pearl hangs from the bottom.

Height overall 3$\frac{15}{16}$ (8.5)
Height of pendant 2$\frac{3}{16}$ (5.6)
Width 1$\frac{3}{8}$ (3.4)
Collections
   Frederic Spitzer
   Maurice Kann
   Jacob Hirsch
Exhibited
   Fogg Art Museum (1937)
   California Palace of the Legion of Honor (1942)
   Detroit Institute of Arts (1958–1959)
Published
   Bonnaffé (1891) III, p. 151, no. 48, ill. pl. 4
   Spitzer Sale (1893) II, p. 49, ill. pl. XLVII, no. 1833
   von Boehn (1929) ill. p. 199
   Fogg (1937) no. 8, ill.
   California Palace (1942) p. 30, no. 205, ill.
   Detroit (1958) no. 368, ill. p. 149
BMA L.62.15.209
Gutman 1251

All the major elements of the frontal composition of this piece have been attached in the same way to a foundation frame, with evident forethought, and the consistency of execution is remarkable. For example, and as can be seen from the back, the pendant consists of a pierced base to which have been bolted the emeralds placed at the springing of the arch, the ruby voussoirs, the emeralds of the plinths, and the bust. The columns, in turn, are bolted to the upper and lower edges of the mounts of the gems at the springing and the plinths beneath the columns. The bust is fastened by a bolt and bent clasp to a vertical splat at the back. The mount of the sapphire beneath the bust has been riveted through the base, as have the flowerets on either side. Thus, all major elements have been attached in the same way to the foundation. There is no reason to question the consistent identification of this piece as Italian, although it is northern, not southern.

34   Pendant of Gold and Enamel with Venus and Cupid

SOUTH GERMAN AND NORTH ITALIAN   LATE 16TH CENTURY

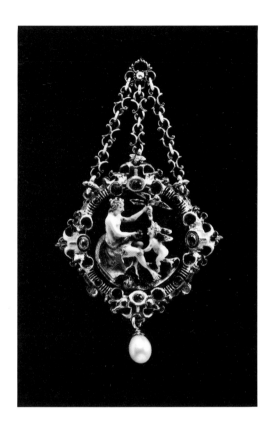

The pendant hangs from an openwork quatrefoil by three chains composed of links of four joined scrolls, each chain has a terminal link of a four-part rosette. The pendant consists of a lozenge-shaped frame, cast and carved. At the four corners, scrolled cartouches, enameled opaque blue and white and topped on the right and left by small fleurs-de-lis, surmount a circular torus molding of opaque black and gold bands, with circular and elliptical applications of translucent red, green and blue, and opaque white and blue enamel. Within the circular aperture is a field of translucent dark blue *en plein* enamel applied over concentric circular carving. This field is the face of a gold plate, a rounded lozenge with foliated edges invisible from the front, which has been attached to the first frame by two rivets at the bottom and the links of the two longer suspension chains at the top. Held to this face by cotters inserted through two slots and bent over in back is a cast, carved and punch-tooled group of Venus and Cupid. Venus sits to the left, with a translucent red enameled apple in her right hand, holding aloft with her left hand a bird. Cupid approaches in profile from the right, his left hand is on Venus' right knee and with his right arm he reaches for the bird. Flesh parts are of opaque white enamel. The crown, bird and wings of Cupid, as well as the landscape, are mottled translucent red and green enamel, the drapery is gold.

Height overall 3¼ (8.2)
Height of medallion 2¼ (5.7)
Width 1⅞ (4.7)
Collections
    National Hungarian Museum
    Baron Nathaniel von Rothschild
Exhibited
    Hungarian National Exhibition (1884)
    Detroit Institute of Arts (1958–1959)
Published
    Pulszky, Radisics, Molinier (1884) p. 78
    Detroit (1958) p. 147, no. 378
BMA L.62.15.200
Gutman 1201a

The Hungarian National Exhibition at Budapest (Pulszky, Radisics, Molinier [1884] p. 78) assigned this piece to Italy, the Detroit Institute of Arts has agreed with the date of 16th century; Mr. Gutman regards it as probably Italian, of the 17th century. None has been able to fix these firmly for the composite nature of the piece makes a confident date and provenance unsafe.

First, the frame itself does not set forth any peculiar characteristics of provenance: there are no gems which might be localized and the design, though certainly Italianate, could be that of any peripatetic craftsman. Second, the blue ground, the concealed border of which does not truly fit the frame, has been adapted to the outer frame. Third, the group of Venus and Cupid, the semicircular base of which does not fit the frame either, is modeled with much greater delicacy than the remainder. It is, indeed, almost *en ronde bosse*, and would seem to be more appropriate to a revealing setting (cf., nos. 30 and 31 in this catalogue) from which the group stood forward, as on a pendant. The cataloguer suggests that the classic-mythological subject-matter of the central group is akin to that made popular by Hans Collaert, Hieronymous Kramer and other late 16th century Northern designers, and that for this portion a designation of "South German, late 16th century" would not be far-fetched. The blue ground is completely anonymous and unlocalized. The frame, however, is rather that of an *enseigne* than a pendant, and could be North Italian rather than South German.

35   Oval Agate Pendant of Orpheus and the Animals

IN THE MANNER OF ALESSANDRO MASNAGO   SECOND HALF OF THE 16TH CENTURY

The frame is suspended by two chains from a two-lobed ring cartouche enameled in opaque black, white and blue, and translucent red and green. The frame is a convex molding with a flat raised band on the face and vertical interior walls. A black and gold arabesque and spiral pattern is interrupted by translucent green enamel leaves with rings holding the links of the two chains. At the bottom a similar translucent green enamel wreath is finished off by a translucent red enamel bead. The band on the face contains opaque blue enamel and a gold dot and dash pattern. The cameo has been almost entirely drill-cut in a varicolored cross section slab of agate containing small encystments of pyrites. Obverse: The entire cameo very cleverly uses the translucent and opaque deposits of the agate. Within a red flecked and ringed white cloud, Orpheus, holding his lyre to the right and striking the strings with a plectrum in the right hand, sits upon a rock approached by a pedestal of three steps and surrounded by a glory of twenty-five rays. The translucent gray agate surrounding the white deposit acts as sky, the remaining reddish brown and brown deposit is carved above, right and left, into clouds and flights of descending birds, and below, into a rocky landscape populated by both wild and domestic animals: an elephant, a camel, a ram, an ox, a goat, a dog, a horse, a lion, a sheep and several unidentifiable beasts. On the reverse, scratched within the central brown portion is the number "130" and repeated near the edge, between the two chain rings, also "130."

Height of medallion 2⁵⁄₁₆ (5.9)
Height overall 4⅝ (11.8)
Width 2⅝ (6.7)
Collection
    F. Mannheimer, Amsterdam
Exhibited
    Detroit Institute of Arts (1958–1959)
Published
    Detroit (1958) no. 367
BMA L.62.15.54
Gutman 1181

The attribution of this exceptionally striking piece, with its imaginative use of the milky-hued translucent band as a cloud, to a specific artist, in this case Alessandro Masnago, is very tempting. The artist, son of Giovanni Antonio Masnago, was active in Milan in the second half of the 16th century, probably under the patronage of Emperor Rudolf II. His *oeuvre*, collected stylistically around a single monogrammed piece in the Kunsthistorisches Museum, Vienna (cf., Kris [1929] 11, pls. 356–363 and Eichler-Kris [1927] pl. 33, nos. 223–226 and pl. 35, nos. 227–229) is especially noteworthy for its sources in Etienne Delaune and for the anti-classical elements introduced from north of the Alps. The animals entering the Ark (Kris [*ibid.*] no. 356) in a piece in Vienna have much the same informal, crowded ar-

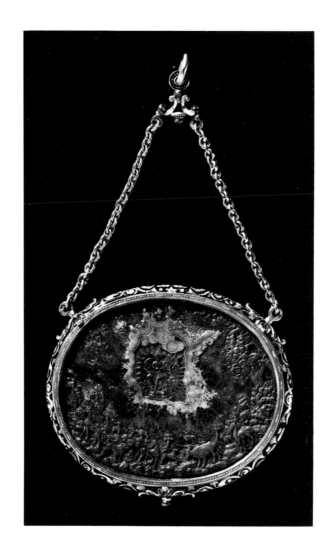

102

rangement as the host attending Orpheus in the Gutman piece, and also in a poorly reproduced example in the Spitzer Collection (1893, no. 1825) which utilizes precisely the same striation of the agate for the same iconography. Kris himself, however, concedes that this inconspicuous artist was followed by an anonymous crowd whose productions cannot be more definitely fixed than "in the manner of."

The handsome carved gold design of the *champlevé* enameled frame relates to the late 16th-early 17th centuries and internationally disseminated projects of many engravers, predominantly Flemish and French (e.g., Jacques Hurter, 1614). The origin of these planographic inventions has not yet been thoroughly explored: they appear to be derived from some kind of workshop residue, like the metal plates left over after other pieces have been cut out. They are characterized by long, thin rectangular shapes which give way suddenly to concavities and which sprout thin, swiftly-curved tendrils ending in volutes. If the frame and cameo are of the same date, this would be added evidence for a follower of Alessandro Masnago.

36   Pendant of Gold, Jewels and Enamel, with Intaglio *Judgment of Paris*

ITALIAN   LATE 16TH CENTURY

The pendant is suspended from a single, cast, gold and black enamel baluster ring by two long chains to the sides and one short chain to the top. The two long chains consist of four double links with square, gold-mounted, table-cut rubies and droplets of red and green translucent enamel at the sides and corners of each square gold mount. The shorter chain, which is attached to a single, cast, gold and white enamel baluster ring at the top of the frame, contains a rectangular gold-mounted, table-cut diamond with red and green enameled droplets at the sides and corners of the mount. The frame consists of two parts. The outside is a cast gold wreath containing ten, equally spaced, table-cut rubies. Each ruby is the center of a flower with six petals of translucent blue enamel between foliage of translucent green enamel and berries or fruit of translucent red enamel. From the sides and bottom are suspended three groups of two pearls each. On the back, the mounts of the rubies and diamond are enameled black with a pattern of four addorsed crescents to each mount. Red, green and blue translucent enamels continue the flower and foliage motif of the front. The outer frame is attached to the frame proper of the intaglio, a band of translucent green enamel over concave pitted tooling, and a raised concave edge enclosing the intaglio itself. The intaglio is an ellipse of semi-translucent, greenish-gray, highly striated, crypto-crystalline quartz. The nude Paris sits on a rock at the left facing Hera, Aphrodite and Athena (all without definite attributes) and holds forward the Apple of Discord, not to the first figure who stands immediately before him, but across in front of her to Aphrodite who stands in the center and reaches forth her left hand to receive it. At the far right the third figure, her back turned, disrobes gracefully and lays her mantle on a rock. A thin tree trunk twines behind Paris and breaks into five sprays of foliage at the top. The exergue beneath the scene is plain.

Height overall 3½ (8.9)
Width 1½ (3.8)
Collections
    Count Michelozzi Giacomini, Florence
    Luigi Grassi
    Henry Walters
Exhibited
    Walters Art Gallery (1948)
    Detroit Institute of Arts (1958–1959)
Published
    Grassi Sale (1927) p. 186, no. 492, ill. p. 187
    Walters Sale (1943) p. 184, no. 989, ill. p. 185
    D'Otrange (1953) p. 133
    Detroit (1958) p. 146, no. 365, ill. p. 148
BMA L.62.15.2
Gutman 595

This piece is of remarkable elegance and the delicacy of its frame is consonant with the execution of the intaglio. Documentation in the owner's possession includes a statement by Pietro Toesca that "the design, the execution, as well as the incising of the gem, all belong to the Florentine art of about the middle of the 16th century, and strongly exhibit the influence of Benvenuto Cellini." However, the reduced and elegant color scheme, with its repeated accents of red and green, is not consonant with the preponderance of North Italian pieces of this period, which lean to a primacy of white, red, light blue and green (cf. mounted cameos in the Kunsthistorisches Museum, Vienna, Rossi [1954] pl. LXIII, c and d). The probably Saxon origin of the intaglio stone would make a North Italian connection likely for the intaglio.

37 Pendant Tetramorph Cameo

FLORENTINE   16TH CENTURY

The frame is suspended by a single gold loop hidden behind the ram's head at the top. The frame consists of two walls, one surrounding the cameo and fluted with small concave channels. This is tightly fitted onto a second, slightly splayed, wall ornamented at the top with a cast and carved ram's head, the horns of which are enameled translucent blue; to right and left, two human faces with horns enameled translucent blue and curved locks of hair enameled translucent red forming volutes attached by solder to the wall of the frame; at the bottom, a horned grotesque with protruding tongue, the horns enameled translucent blue, the tongue red. In between these decorations are alternate oval and circular panels of translucent green and opaque white enamel between a thin border of opaque black lines. The back is hollow to the cameo, and the cameo presents, left, profile head of a bearded man and right, profile head of a young man; top, a ram's head in profile, and bottom a satyr's head in profile. The ram's horns form a central volute connecting all four profiles. At the top of the cameo are two small chips in the edge and at bottom right a slight superficial crack. From the reverse it can be clearly seen that the frame surrounding the cameo is soldered to its mate from behind. The four heads attached to the second section are very strongly modeled and seem to have been worked separately and then fused to the band. The point of fusion has been almost obliterated by subsequent tooling previous to the application of enamel.

Height 1⅞₆ (3.7)
Width 1¼ (3.2)
Collections
   Luigi Grassi
   Henry Walters
Exhibited
   Walters Art Gallery (1948)
   Art Institute of Chicago (1951–1962) RX200/3
Published
   Grassi Sale (1927) no. 479, ill. p. 182
   Walters Sale (1941) II, p. 398, no. 1277
   D'Otrange (1952) p. 72, ill. p. 70
BMA L.52.15.73
Gutman 588

All previous expertise has agreed that the cameo is of Graeco-Roman workmanship and the frame is Florentine, 16th century. D'Otrange (1952, p. 72, ill. p. 70) interprets the composition as "four heads: an old man, a youth, a faun and a ram. The symbolism of the two ages of man and their ruling passions is obvious, and versions of both the faun and the ram have been used in the frame also, but with the profiles of the two men replaced by purely decorative masks." The documentation of the Art Institute of Chicago mentions that the four heads are "centered by [a] snail." An analytical examination suggests, however, that the solution may be elsewhere. The horn (not a snail) belongs to the youthful profile, right, identifying this visage as that of Zeus-Ammon (Alexander the Great in this guise). Also, being centered in the design, the intention may be to share it with all four faces, as a common attribute. The "faun" seems to be something like a profile portrait of Socrates: there are no clearly identifying horns here. The ram's or sheep's head may be one symbol out of four, or it may be an attributive head-covering analagous to the lion of Hercules, making the composition tripartite.

Professor Peter H. von Blanckenhagen of the Institute of Fine Arts, New York University, thinks the piece is "definitely Renaissance" and speaking of this piece (as well as a related piece, no. 42) writes: "There is a certain allusion to Zeus-Ammon and Alexander, but neither portrait really fits and the entire composition has, to my knowledge, no ancient parallel. Both gems seem to me characteristic pieces of that 16th century learning which so often invented 'ancient' compositions." In any case, the iconographic complexity leaves one certain that the cameo, together with the frame, is a Renaissance interpretation of a Graeco-Roman stone of the type made to be viewed from any direction. One might speculate that the symbolism conveys the antithesis of *Intellectus-Ignorantia*, humanity-bestiality or some such favorite Renaissance polarity, or the four temperaments and four elements. The consonance of the frame itself with the interior tends to substantiate this conjecture. And, while there is no explicit reason for calling the frame Florentine, if the cameo is Renaissance it is precisely the sort of allusive composite that would have been confected through the effect of the Platonic Academy, and the entire piece would reasonably be called a fine Florentine jewel.

38

Pendant of Gold, Enamel and Pearls: An Armed Centaur

SPANISH   CA. 1600

The pendant is suspended by four plain, linked gold chains of equal length from a four-part cluster of volutes enameled opaque black, white and blue. Within the space between the spirals are four translucent green enameled leaves and four translucent red enameled berries. From the bottom depends a single pin-fastened pearl. The human half of the centaur's body consists of a hollow cast and carved gold head, torso and arms. The head wears an opaque black enameled helmet, and the face, with short beard, is carefully and emphatically modeled. In his right hand he holds a spear (restored). The equine forequarters and hindquarters are of opaque white enamel over a hollow cast and carved gold base. The remaining part of the beast is a large baroque pearl. This figure has been fused to a base of opaque green enamel, bordered with volutes and scrolls enameled opaque black, blue and white. This base is attached separately by means of two bolt fastenings to the translucent green enameled surface of the oval frame beneath. Also attached to this surface, and surrounding the base, are six small flower clusters of translucent red, green and lavender enamel. This oval gold base, bordered with a torus molding of black enamel with opaque white ovals and circles, has four translucent green enameled cartouches which serve as the rings for the suspension pins. Hinged to this and opening downward is a concave *ajouré* section of strapwork volutes and flowers, enameled opaque white and blue, and translucent green, red and dark blue. From the bottom is suspended, by an enameled baluster ring, a large oval pearl.

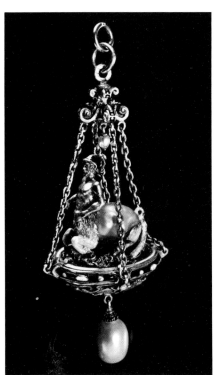

Height excluding two top rings 3⁷⁄₁₆ (8.7)
Width 1½ (3.8)
Collection
    Baron Max von Goldschmidt-Rothschild
Exhibited
    Detroit Institute of Arts (1958–1959)
Published
    Goldschmidt-Rothschild Sale (1950) 11, no. 98, ill. p. 25
    Detroit (1958) no. 366, p. 146
BMA L.62.15.214
Gutman unnumbered

The provenances assigned to this uncommonly fine piece are already disparate. The catalogue of the Goldschmidt-Rothschild sale (1950) gives it to Nürnberg, ca. 1600. It was included, without further justification, in the Detroit catalogue (1958, no. 366).

The base of a pendant in the Waddesdon Bequest (1902, p. 78, no. 165) of a parrot enameled green and set with clusters of rubies, is so similar as to suggest that both pieces originated in the same workshop. The enameled flowers of the upper plate, the pierced strapwork scrolls and the fastening of the pendant pearl are nearly identical. The parrot is called South German, 16th century (there are no additional annotations in the British Museum catalogue). The baroque pearl body at once brings to mind the Canning Jewel, ca. 1580, in the Victoria and Albert Museum, which Evans (1953, p. 24, pl. 73a) moots as "perhaps Italian."

On the grounds of resemblance between the subject matter of the Gutman piece and another of the Barcelona silversmiths' guild-book drawings (Johnson [1963] fig. 23) and another centaur, comparatively crudely worked, in the collection of the Hispanic Society of America (*ibid.*, fig. 1) it is suggested that the Gutman pendant and its companion, the parrot of the Waddesdon Bequest, are both Spanish of about 1600.

39

Pendant of Gold, Enamel and Semiprecious Stones: A Mermaid

SPANISH   LATE 16TH CENTURY

The pendant is suspended by two identical chains from a cast and carved single-ringed cartouche, enameled translucent red and green, and opaque white, from the center of which hangs a single pin-fastened pearl on a baluster mount with white enamel droplets. In the center of the cartouche is a hemispherical collet-mounted garnet. The chains consist of two rosettes each connected by single plain links. The eight-leaved rosettes, enameled translucent red and green, center similarly cut smaller garnets. The bottom links are attached to rings in the shoulders of the mermaid. The mermaid is a hollow cast, carved and tooled figure with upraised left hand with a single pin-fastened pearl suspended from a wrist bracelet, and lowered right hand holding the link of a second pin-fastened pearl. Her high coiffure is embellished with six cabochon-cut garnets and opaque white and translucent green enamel. Draped over her shoulders and around her arms is a translucent blue enamel scarf, which becomes a single volute at the right elbow. As a brooch fastening the scarf at the breast is a very dark cabochon-cut garnet in a carved quatrefoil mount. The center of the body is a large elliptical cabochon of highly polished, mottled red, gray, black and white jasper in a simple beveled frame surrounded by opaque white enamel. On either side two fins, or wings, enameled translucent red and green, are attached to the body by tenons through the seam of the two halves of the cast. The back and tail are enameled translucent green, with a sash of fruit and flowers enameled translucent red. Cabochon-cut garnets and cloudy rose quartz stones in the tail complete the ensemble.

Height 4³⁄₁₆ (10.6)
Width 1¹³⁄₁₆ (4.6)
Exhibited
    Walters Art Gallery (1948)
BMA L.62.15.166
Gutman 894

This piece is as lavish with respect to the materials it provides for discussion as its creator was in the use of the materials at his disposal for realizing his designs. A very close parallel is afforded by another pendant in the form of a mermaid in the Waddesdon Bequest, British Museum (no. 154, B.M./W.B. 1902, pl. XXXVII), called German or Spanish, 16th century, "in the style of Erasmus Hornick." The annotated Waddesdon Bequest catalogue in the Department of British and Medieval Antiquities in the British Museum has the following superscription: "Dr. E. Kris says *Spanish*. Cf., perhaps Salting Bequest jewel set with emeralds and rubies in form of a pelican: pearl hanging above head, another below tail. M536–1910." The Salting Bequest jewel is illustrated in Steingräber (1956, fig. 200) and Salting (1926, pl. XIII, 1).

The most striking points of similarity between the Gutman piece and the Waddesdon Bequest mermaid are: the volute at the left elbow, the upraised right hand, the disposition of jewels along the lower trunk and tail, and the rounded tail fin. The Waddesdon Bequest piece lacks the wing-fins, but these, in turn, are similar in turn to the wings of the Salting Bequest "pelican." Both the disposition of jewels and the wings are combined in a drawing of a "winged dragon" (Palm's more accurate designation of the Salting Bequest "pelican"), now lost, in the anonymous inventory of Treasury of Guadalupe, 1778 (Palm [1951] fig. 13).

All this would seem to weight both the Waddesdon Bequest and Gutman mermaids in favor of Spain, save that the former, when in the Londesborough Collection (see Waddesdon Bequest [1902] p. 75, no. 154 for reference) holds a large hand-mirror in her now empty left hand, *Loreleiweise*. Of the stones employed decoratively the central jasper cabochon doubtless served a therapeutic purpose. The stone was considered effective against the colic, according to Alexander Trallianus, a Greek physician of the first half of the 6th century, and de Boot (1536, pp. 251–253) strenuously recommended its use in checking fluxes and hemorrhages. Such a use was common in Italy among the peasantry within the present century according to Bellucci. (For these references on jasper as a healing stone, see Kunz [1915] pp. 144–145.)

The sanguinary color of the garnets and rose quartz might be a sympathetic re-enforcement of this traditional power. The anatomical placement of the stone could be interpreted as a defense against female complaints which, even in a mermaid, it would be indelicate to specify. On the other hand, St. Jerome assigns to jasper a potent talismanic force (*Opera omnia*, ed. Migne, IV, cols. 544–545), especially the variety known as *grammatias*, the mottlings of which resembled letters of the alphabet and were thought to be a spell, "writ large by Nature's hand," against phantoms and *pavor nocturnus*.

40 Pendant of Gold, Enamel, Diamonds and Pearls: A Mermaid

SPANISH COLONIAL   EARLY 17TH CENTURY

The figure is suspended by two chains from a cartouche ornamented in back and front by two rectangular table-cut diamonds. The left-hand chain consists of two fleur-de-lis links with a link bearing two table-cut diamonds on either side; the right-hand chain attached to the end of the tail is of simple gold links and three seed pearls. The figure is wax cast and, to judge from the weight, almost solid. Only a slight amount of reworking is visible: in the hair at the back and in the grooves of the scales. The head has a crown with three table-cut diamonds, two above the ears and one in the center. The right hand holds a sceptre surmounted by an oval pin-fastened pearl. The lower part of the body is embellished with scales of translucent green enamel and a skirt, or *tutu*, of opaque white enamel with traces of pink and black painted enamel. The tail ends in a fleur-de-lis, from the two arms of which are suspended seed pearls. Another seed pearl is suspended from a gold fin at the bottom.

Height 2¹¹⁄₁₆ (6.9)
Width 1⅞ (4.8)
Collection
    Alfred de Rothschild
Exhibited
    Art Institute of Chicago (1951–1962) RX200/54
BMA L.62.15.122
Gutman 1059

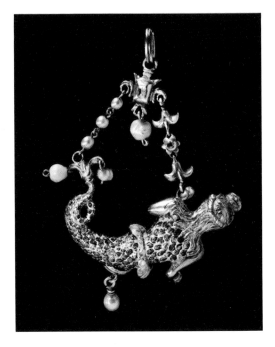

112

The provenance of this piece has eluded precise determination. It offers to the eye a contrast of intrinsic and extrinsic worth that is puzzling, and suggestive of an extraordinary origin. Both the Art Institute of Chicago and Mr. Gutman have called it Italian, with a question mark, of the late 16th century, but their hesitation is understandable, for, unless it is a provincial work which at the same time is of extraordinarily prodigal substance, seemingly of solid gold, this attribution is not particularly appealing.

First, the technical skill exhibited is not that of the normal Renaissance craftsman practicing in either a naturalistic or classicistic tradition. The modelling of the face, for example, is mask-like, taut and outside European conventions. Second, the gold remains to a preponderant degree unfashioned beyond the pristine pitted surface, indicating either an indifference to further refinement or the want of hard, sharp carving tools. Third, more gold has been used to produce the figure than even the most extravagant Renaissance craftsman would have considered well-advised. Such relative lavishness and relative crudity together cannot be easily fitted into the late 16th century European professional scheme of things.

If we can assume that Spain is one of the major sources of these mermaid pendants (cf. no. 39) then one of the Spanish colonies in the New World would provide both the surplus of material used and the inexperienced format. Since the casting is not of a quality to be consistent with Panama, the cataloguer suggests Peru or Mexico, with a later date of early 17th century.

41 Pendant in Gold, Enamel, Baroque Pearls and Diamonds: A Unicorn

ITALIAN   CA. 1575–1580

The pendant is suspended by two chains of double links from a single ring to which is attached a single pin-fastened pearl. The body of the unicorn consists of a large baroque pearl of bluish luster. To this has been attached the two hollow cast and carved gold and enameled parts of the unicorn's body: head, neck and lower part of the body including legs and tail. Except for the twisted horn which bears traces of opaque dark green enamel, the gold parts of the body are covered by a network of lozenges filled with a coarse, pitted, white enamel which apparently contained some odd mixture of combustible impurity to give to the surface, once fired, a naturalistic, dappled finish. Compartments from which the enamel is now missing are filled with some kind of hard resinous material. The calves of the fore and back legs, tail, muzzle, ears and mane are plain gold. The eyes are two small diamonds, one rose-cut, one fancy-cut. From a ring in the unicorn's belly is suspended one elongated baroque pearl in an eight-leaved silver mount, much tarnished, set with sixteen fancy-cut diamonds. A second pin-fastened pearl depends from a ring in the chest.

Height of Unicorn, including pearl drop 1⅞ (4.8)
Width from horn tip 1¹³⁄₁₆ (4.6)
Collection
    Baron Max von Goldschmidt-Rothschild
Exhibited
    Art Institute of Chicago (1951–1962) RX200/72
Published
    Goldschmidt-Rothschild Sale (1950) II, p. 24, no. 97
    D'Otrange (1952) p. 70, ill. p. 69
    Stone (1959) p. 108, fig. VII

Previous attributions of provenance by the Goldschmidt-Rothschild sale catalogue (1950), D'Otrange (1952), the Art Institute of Chicago and Peter Stone (1959) are all consistent in their citations of Italy; the only disagreement is in respect to date. All except the Goldschmidt-Rothschild catalogue, which gives it to the early 17th century, prefer a date of mid-16th century. The cataloguer would like, if only on the basis of style, to compromise between these two. The piece, though admittedly much less intricate as a composition, seems to succeed, rather than to precede, the sculpturesque and three-dimensional designs of Erasmus Hornick and Hans Collaert. Were it mid-16th century one is inclined to think that the figure would have been a half-figure, divided lengthwise, with a backing of engraved and enameled gold. Were it after 1600, somewhere the fleeter, more nimble delicacy of the Mignot-Rouillart-Carteron inventions would be displayed. Thus a date of ca. 1575–1580 is put forward to bring the piece into consonance with similar free-hanging pendants of like date.

42 Pendant Cameo of an Imperial Figure with Divine Attributes in Gold, Enamel and Pearl Frame

ITALIAN OR ENGLISH   LATE 16TH AND EARLY 17TH CENTURIES

The oval frame is a cast and carved, slightly convex band which provides a thin retaining flange for the cameo. The basic band is enameled with two stripes, one narrow of opaque white, and one wide of opaque black. Riveted to this band are three strap-work cartouches, enameled opaque white and blue, and translucent red, with pin-fastened seed pearls in the center, and a somewhat larger cartouche of similar design at the top, with central ring and two gold loops. Four quatrefoil flowerettes, enameled opaque white and translucent red, also centered with pin-fastened seed pearls, are disposed between the cartouches. The cameo is cut in three layers of opaque banded, dyed agate, ranging from brown to bluish gray to gray. Within a thin frame of brown the athletic figure of a nearly nude male, turned three-quarters left, head in profile, holds in his right hand a thunderbolt (?) and in his left hand a staff. An eagle, three-quarters left but with head turned backward toward the figure, is at his feet at left. The figure is draped with the aegis, which is caught over the left elbow and falls behind the stave; his curly hair is bound with a diadem. On the back of the cameo, centered, are the numbers 736 in white pigment.

Height from stationary loop 2⅞ (7.3)
Width 2¼ (5.7)
Collections
   Earl of Arundel
   George, Duke of Marlborough
   David Bromilow, Esq.
   Mrs. Jary
   Sir Francis Cook, Bart.
   Humphrey W. Cook, Esq.
   Dr. Jacob Hirsch
   Joseph Brummer
Exhibited
   Art Institute of Chicago (1951–1962) RX200/60
Published
   Marlborough Gems Sale (1899), p. 2, no. 4
   H. W. Cook Sale (1925) p. 203, no. 203
   Brummer Sale (1949) II, p. 54, no. 238, ill. p. 55
   D'Otrange (1952) p. 69
   Hackenbroch (1954) pl. 94
BMA L.62.15.128
Gutman 1096

The pedigree and documentation of this piece are so impressive that one becomes hesitant in voicing reservations. The cameo has been accepted as Roman from the outset, albeit twice published erroneously as at once of Claudius and of the 1st century B.C. The personage becomes Claudius only after 1899, when, in the Catalogue of the Marlborough Gems he is described with rather less presumption as "probably . . . an emperor, perhaps Augustus himself." The present frame and the cameo cannot be connected before this date. Thus the questions which should be answered are: 1) Is the cameo Roman? 2) Who is the figure? 3) Is the frame Renaissance and, if so, 4) does the frame belong with the cameo from the outset?

The physical habitus displayed by the figure, with its combination of sinuosity and theatrical muscular emphasis, is late Hellenistic. Roman realistic tastes colliding with this tradition produced such odd mutations as the "Unknown Man" from Delos, found in 1894 and now in the National Museum, Athens (no. 1928). Here the figure, as in most such late Hellenistic works, is nude; a mantle is slung over the back. Conversely, a pre-imperial portrait in the Roman tradition would have presented the figure either fully draped or with an ampler accumulation of drapery around the hips and legs. The aegis depicted in the present cameo is a kind of displaced stole; yet the quality is such that this device cannot be laid to technical deficiency. The argument must be suggested that if the cameo is pre-imperial, the figure should be nude; if imperial, either nude or more fully and truly draped than it is.

The covering actually suggests prudishness rather than modesty—a post-Tridentine obsession. Jupiter, with attributes of eagle and thunderbolt, the figure is certainly intended to be—yet, as has been pointed out by Prof. Erik Sjöqvist of Princeton University, Zeus should not be toying with a caduceus in his left hand (if that is what the object is intended to represent). Frances F. Jones, Chief Curator and Curator of Classical Art of The Art Museum, Princeton University, cites incongruous details "which

117

imply a post-classical date: animal skin where one expects cloth drapery and what seems to be a caduceus in the left hand of a figure in the patent guise of Jupiter." Dorothy Kent Hill of the Walters Art Gallery sees the caduceus as a sceptre; she observes: "The wearing of a loin cloth is not unusual, but the use of an aegis for this purpose is surprising, and the aegis is unduly big . . . The style seems to me un-antique."

That it can also be Claudius, the crippled stammerer, is barely possible, in view of the conservative tradition of the Julio-Claudian house. Nonetheless the head appears to be based on the Windsor Castle Claudius and is a good likeness. It is not based on the Vatican Claudius. The preference of the classical cameo-cutter was for an unframed plane. Where the composition is framed, it is usually by a single moulding. These qualifications, each perhaps slight in itself, add up to a credible Renaissance origin for the cameo. Moreover the style of the figure suggests a follower of Michelangelo.

In view of the provenance, given as the Earl of Arundel, in England, and the relationship with the Windsor Castle Claudius, an origin in the 17th century English is suggested.

The frame holds the piece very insecurely. The retaining flange in back has been recut and pressed around the edges of the cameo and there is far too much open space around the outer surfaces in front to vouch for the frame's being coadunate. The deep convexity of the rear of the frame leads to the suggestion that it is one half of a two part reliquary or devotional locket, probably early 17th century, of the type of no. 13 in this catalogue, though of Italian origin.

118

43 Pendant Double-faced Cameo of Juno (?) and Minerva in Enameled and Jeweled Gold Frame

ENGLISH   CA. 1580

The frame of this double-faced, carnelian cameo is a diamond-shaped, open-work arrangement of cartouches and fleurs-de-lis suspended from a single ring. A fleur-de-lis at the top, which holds the ring, is enameled opaque white with two translucent green enamel central leaves. On either side of this, and symmetrically placed at the bottom, are four fleurs-de-lis of opaque white enamel with central leaves of translucent red enamel finished off at the base with quatrefoil rosettes of opaque blue enamel. Center left and right are cartouches in white and translucent red; and at the bottom, a cartouche of opaque white enamel from which is suspended a single pearl with translucent red enamel mount. At top, bottom, left and right, four collet-mounted, table-cut transparent stones, apparently quartz replacements. The oval gold frame, tooled with a small convex punch, encloses a cameo of Juno (?). Reverse: relatively flat back of design enameled in opaque blue and white with translucent red and green. Four square gold rivets in translucent green enamel mounts hold collet mounts of obverse. Oval carnelian cameo of Minerva, facing right.

Height overall 2⅟₁₆(6.5)
Width 1¾ (4.5)
Collection
    Henry Symonds
Exhibited
    Walters Art Gallery (1948)
    Detroit Institute of Arts (1958–1959)
Published
    Detroit (1958) p. 147, no. 375, ill. p. 148
BMA L.62.15.56
Gutman 605

The provenance of this piece, formerly reckoned Italian, must be shifted to one rarer and more precious. It may, on excellent grounds, be assigned to England and to the late Elizabethan period, about 1580. The coloration of the enamel, with its predominance of opaque white accented by translucent red and blue, is paralleled in the Barbor Jewel in the Victoria and Albert Museum (Evans [1921] p. 97, pl. XIX, 4) said to have been made after the accession of Elizabeth (1558) to commemorate the deliverance through that event of William Barbor from the stake at Smithfield. White enamel as an English setting for cameos is mentioned in the inventory of John Mabbe, who, in 1576, was given special permission to sell his stock of jewels made with gold of less than twenty-two carats; these included "a broache with a very fayr Agott like a Blackamore enamelled all white about the said agott" (T. Rymer in *Foedera, apud* Evans [1921] pp. 97–98 and fn. 1). White enamel is conspicuous in the Heneage Jewel, given to Sir Thomas Heneage by Queen Elizabeth, dating about 1588, in the Victoria and Albert Museum.

The careful finishing of both sides of the gem is also indicative of English workmanship, and the separation of the cameos from the decorative border by two complete frames, isolating the image, conforms to English workmanship (Evans [1953] p. 130). The Elizabethan character of the design is strongly upheld by comparing this piece to the frame of the miniature on the skirt of Mary Cornwallis in a portrait attributed to George Gower (fl. 1579–1596) in the City Art Gallery, Manchester (*Burlington Magazine*, Vol. CVI, no. 736, July, 1964, fig. 1).

The heads illustrated of Juno and Minerva, if so identifiable, may be taken to symbolize feminine intellectuality and domesticity.

44 Pendant Locket with Agate Cameo of Queen Elizabeth in Gold, Enamel and Pearl Frame.

ENGLISH   BETWEEN 1582 AND 1588   *Color plate opposite*

The frame is suspended from a single ring by three chains with flat links, the center chain being interrupted by a single seed pearl. The frame is basically a hollow, cast and carved oval half-cylinder. The decoration of the frame is almost unique in that it is fully and symmetrically carried out on obverse and reverse. At the top, bottom, left and right are four *ajouré* interlocked strapwork volutes, enameled opaque white, black and turquoise blue, and translucent red and green. The top volute is surmounted by a baluster ring holding the central chain, the base of which is a coronet, topped with opaque white pellets. Two square, table-cut rubies in high collet mounts are centered obverse and reverse between the volutes. The bottom volute has a similar arrangement, from the ring of which is suspended a single, pin-fastened spherical pearl of fine lustre. To left and right the volutes are the same but the baluster ring and coronet is supplanted by another slightly larger square, table-cut ruby in a high fluted collet mount. The exterior profile of the frame is a central torus molding with two shallower torus moldings on either side. The central molding, through which are fastened the volutes just described, has gold arabesques and oval panels with enameling of opaque white and translucent green.

122

44

The translucent green panels are underneath the volutes. In between the volutes are four coronets of eight pellets of turquoise blue enamel. These, at top, left and right, surround the baluster rings of the left and right suspension chains. Those left and right at bottom surround baluster bosses, enameled with a flecked opaque white. The side moldings, obverse and reverse, have ten long oval panels of translucent blue *basse-taille* enamel between designs of opaque white. The cameo, of banded translucent gray, white and brown sardonyx, presents the breast length profile of the Queen, to left. The portrait is cut through six striae ranging from brown (topmost) to nearly transparent gray at the bottom. The Queen wears a jeweled cap on the back part of her head and a high, full-throated quilled ruff above a jeweled collar. The bodice of her costume is covered with, apparently, brocaded arabesques and another chain falls from the shoulders. Part of the puff of the left sleeve is visible. Reverse: the cameo is replaced by a slightly concave oval panel of translucent grayish agate or feldspar with a top hinge and bottom mortise-and-tenon snap fastener, beneath which is the hollow interior of the frame. Engraved in the surface, above and below a central four-lobed rosette, the initials: CR (top) SM (bottom).

Height including loop 2⅞ (7.3)
Width 1⁷⁄₁₆ (3.6)
Collection
    Baron Max von Goldschmidt-Rothschild
Exhibited
    Art Institute of Chicago (1951–1962) RX200/67
Published
    D'Otrange (1952) ill. p. 70
BMA L.62.15.135
Gutman 1139

For this excellent and well-preserved jewel, the same evidence and parallels adduced for No. 43 may be cited, with the additional reminder that the disposition of the enamel and gems here so closely resembles the Heneage Jewel, and the cameo is so close to the Garter Badge of 1582, that the Gutman jewel can be dated between 1582 and 1588. Even the intaglio flower, cut in the locket-lid of the back, has its counterpart in the rose enameled in the same position in the Heneage Jewel. A pendant similar to the present one is reported by Charles Oman (letter of 4 January 1964) as having been acquired recently by the Victoria and Albert Museum.

45 Rock Crystal Pendant Portrait of Anna Maria of Austria in Gold, Glass and Enamel Frame

SPANISH (?) AND FRENCH   CA. 1570 AND CA. 1620

The portrait is intaglio cut by wheel, gouge, drill and a V chisel in an absolutely flawless oval sheet of rock crystal slightly less than 6 mm. thick. The Queen is shown three-quarter profile to left; she wears a circular brimmed cap with soft crown, a quilled ruff, and suspended from her neck a double headed eagle pendant. Underneath the legend: D:ANNA MARLE D'AVSTRICE·R:D'SPAGE··. The frame consists basically of two torus moldings enameled opaque black with thin gold bands punctuated by gold ovals. On the obverse and reverse the torus molding splays into a scotia holding the obverse and reverse of the crystal. The vertical edge of the crystal is surrounded by a flat band made invisible by the glass bolsters mentioned below. This basic frame of two parts, identical obverse and reverse, is held in place around the crystal by four interlocking tenons, top, bottom, left and right, masked by the cartouches described below and held in place by the screws forming the suspension ring of the top cartouche, the central beads of the cartouches, left and right, and the suspension ring of the pendant pearl at the bottom. The top suspension ring has been rendered immovable by means of glue and a tamped gold filling; the other screws are removable. The two frames, and the vertical edge of the crystal, thus form a low, right angle channel divided into four segments into which fit four bolsters of aquamarine blue transparent glass, evidently sawed half-sections of tubing. Each one of these bears a delicate design of *émail en résille*. On either side of a translucent red, white centered, flower, are symmetrical leaves of translucent dark green and quatrefoil flowers of opaque yellow, centered with white, surrounded by scrolls of translucent red and opaque white and flanked by leaf shapes of opaque green. Each one of these bolsters is held in place by a cast and carved cartouche enameled opaque white and black, and translucent red, green and dark blue. The cartouche is internally concave so that each fits snugly over the surface of the glass bolster. The bottom cartouche is held in place by a screw pin from the ring head of which is suspended a pin-fastened pearl between translucent red enamel mounts.

Height 3⅝ (9.2)
Width 2⁷⁄₁₆ (6.2)
Collection
    Martin J. Desmoni, Esq.
Published
    Desmoni Sale (1960) p. 33, no. 93, ill. pl. 17
BMA L.63.2.244
Gutman 1433

The frame of this pendant is of such grace, frailty and finish that its manufacture by an accomplished craftsman for a court personage must almost be taken for granted. Evans (1953, pp. 139–140) states that the technique used in this frame, *émail en résille sur verre*, is "so difficult that it was only practised for a decade or so, and probably only by one or two exceptionally skilled enamelers, who seem to have worked in France. The only engraved designs that are recognizably intended for it, are, however, those published by Valentin Sezenius between 1619 and 1624." The coloristic and decorative characteristics of these pieces are well marked. They consist of conventionalized and fairly simple flower patterns and arabesques of brilliant, fine-grained opaque enamel preferentially buttercup yellow, white and grass green, with accents of carmine and light blue. Instead of being connected by a network of planographic designs derived from engravers' designs, these opaque enamel elements stand unencumbered within the deeper blue, or blue-green, of the translucent glass base. This relative simplicity must be considered a practical result of the technique's difficulty.

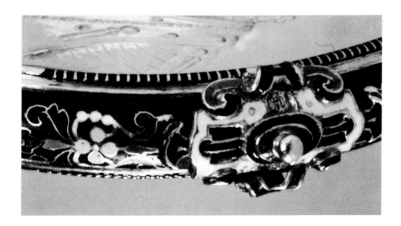

A locket now in the Victoria and Albert Museum (no. M. 65–1952, gift of Dr. Joan Evans. See Evans [1953] pl. VII, a) shows this usual arrangement to perfection; it is described in the Victoria and Albert Register for 1952 as French, "about 1620." An oblong pendant in the Waddesdon Bequest in the British Museum (W.B. 169) a composite and partly 19th century work, contains a plaque of Apollo pursuing Daphne, in the same technique (Evans [1953] pl. 97, b). The figures are surrounded by a wreath in which the flower petals are self-sufficient and accented, upon the translucent blue enamel, in the same colors. The back of a case containing an engraved silver portrait, also of Mary of Austria, formerly in the Pierpont Morgan Collection, reproduces the same scalloped opaque white curves that occur in the Victoria and Albert locket and the Gutman pendant.

The inscription on the rock crystal portrait declares it to be Anna Maria of Austria, Queen of Spain. This would be Anna, fourth wife of Philip II, the daughter of Maximilian II of Austria and the Empress Doña Maria. She was born in Cigales on November 1, 1549, married her uncle Philip II in Segovia, November 14, 1570, and died at Badajoz on October 26, 1580. Two portraits, one in the Prado (no. 1141), a copy from Antonio Moro by Bartolomé Gonzalez, and one in the Kunsthistorisches Museum Vienna, by Sanchez-Coello (Davenport [1948] p. 466, no. 1231), confirm the general, if not specific likeness. The likeness dates probably shortly before or after her marriage: the same type of narrow neck ruff and small cap on the back of parted hair is seen in the portrait of Elizabeth of Austria, ca. 1571, in the Louvre.

The inscription itself, in somewhat rugged French, sets certain difficulties. If the crystal was engraved about 1570, the frame must have been made for it in France some forty years later. Yet it seems odd that a French engraver practicing the excellent technique of the portrait should have misspelled "MARIE" and used a contractile AN to misspell "ESPAGNE." If the portrait is contemporary with the frame, the question arises as to why it should have been done, perhaps thirty years after the Queen's death, during another's reign. An inscription which is contemporary with both the Gutman frame and another of *émail en résille sur verre* is that of the Morgan portrait (Williamson [1910] p. 157, no. 116, pl. xciv) engraved by Simon de Pass between about 1616 and 1622, but here the "V" is consistently "U" and "AVSTRICE" becomes "AUSTRIA." If the present portrait was engraved in Spain, ca. 1570, why is the inscription French? If it was engraved in France at the same time the frame was made, why the defective orthography? Possibly these lapses are by a Spanish engraver, working from a French model provided with the frame.

46 Opal Cameo Portrait Pendant in Oval Gold and Enamel Frame

ENGLISH (ITALIAN?) CA. 1580

The oval gold frame is suspended by a single ring enameled opaque white. The frame proper is a striated, convex gold baluster with opaque black and translucent green arabesques and ovals between four symmetrically placed cartouches top, bottom, left and right. On the reverse a flat band of opaque blue and translucent green and red enamel. At the bottom, suspended by a pin with translucent green and red mounts, a single pearl. The cameo itself presents a profile portrait facing right of a woman in widow's snood, high choker ruff and dress with shoulder puffs. The material of the cameo is thick matrix opal, the iridescent face of which predominates in the background. There are flecks of iridescence in nose, lips and right hand part of the ruff of the dress. The reverse of the cameo is blank.

Height from stationary loop through pearl drop 2⁹⁄₁₆ (6.5)
Width 1⁷⁄₁₆ (3.7)
Collections
    Alice de Rothschild
    Henry Symonds
Exhibited
    Walters Art Gallery (1948)
    Detroit Institute of Arts (1958–1959)
Published
    Detroit (1958) p. 147, no. 374
BMA L.62.15.57
Gutman 602

Published as Italian, second half of the 16th century, by the Detroit Institute of Arts, the frame of this jewel with its simple, carved, gold torus molding and four clasping cartouches, could as well be English; the coloration of the enamel is equally non-specific. The portrait has been taken to be that of Mary, Queen of Scots. Apart from the lack of resemblance between this and other cameo portraits of the Queen (cf. Evans [1953] pl. 84) it seems unlikely that an opal cameo of the Queen would have been cut presenting her as a widow in early middle age. Most extant cameo portraits of her are dated before her abdication in 1567. She was a prisoner in Sheffield Castle from 1569 to 1584, and, though the small portraits of herself and James VI in the Penicuik Locket in the National Museum of Antiquities of Scotland may be dated between 1576 and 1579, and opals became fashionable in England after 1573 (Nichols [1823] I, p. 380) it is only barely plausible that an expensive stone would have been made available for an English portrait of an enemy of the Crown. An English provenance for the cameo, and a date of about 1580, during Mary's lifetime is, however, perfectly acceptable, but the sitter must remain, for the present, anonymous.

128

47   Pendant of a Mounted Warrior in Gold, Enamel, Diamonds and Pearls

SOUTH GERMAN   LATE 16TH CENTURY   *Color plate facing page 168*

The pendant is suspended from a cartouche by two chains of plain gold links. The cartouche comprises three separate sections riveted together through the center. Section one is the cartouche proper, of two narrow volutes set face to face, enameled in opaque white with open-work arabesques of translucent red. Section two is a four-lobed flower of translucent green enamel, the lobes separated by slender, pointed, opaque black enamel spears or leaves. Section three is the flower center, a table-cut diamond in rectangular gold collet. The back of the cartouche is enameled opaque white and translucent green. A single pin-fastened pearl, split nearly in half, with the heart exposed, is suspended from a ring at the bottom. The pendant is a hollow, cast and carved horse and armed rider, both facing left. The horse's mane, mouth, ears, tail, hoofs and harness are gold; the remainder of the body is covered with opaque white enamel except for the opaque black eyes. On the neck, left shoulder, left rear flank, and underneath the belly are four table-cut diamonds in rectangular collet mounts; from the mount under the belly is suspended a single pin-fastened iridescent pearl. The rider is seated upon a translucent red enamel saddle. He wears an opaque blue enamel cuirass and kilt with black enameled lappets, black buskins with blue tops and a crested helmet of opaque black. His right hand wields a scimitar with a table-cut, collet-mounted diamond on the hilt. His left hand holds a small buckler in the form of a modified cross *pattée*, of translucent red enamel, centered with a table-cut diamond in collet mount. Both his chest and the front of the helmet bear similar diamonds. Behind the helmet, draped over the left and right elbows, billows gold drapery with a table-cut diamond at its apogee. The shield and drapery have been cast separately and attached by flanges and bending to the figure. Horse and rider are hollow cast, and held together by the bolt through the center, which also serves as the base for the table-cut diamond under the horse's belly. The tail is separately cast and soldered to the body. The quality of the enamel is similar to Mr. Gutman's piece no. 1161, though the pitting is less conspicuous.

Height overall 3⁷⁄₁₆ (9)
Height of horse and rider 1⅞ (4.8)
Width 1⅝ (4.2)
Exhibited
    Detroit Institute of Arts (1958–1959)
Published
    Detroit (1958) p. 146, no. 370
BMA L.62.15.205
Gutman 1220

This pendant is extraordinary in the spirited, skillful and realistic modeling and the finesse of the enamel work. A slightly larger pendant in the Waddesdon Bequest at the British Museum (1902, no. 161, pl. XXXVI) there called "German, 16th Century," is so similar as to point to the same workshop.

The principle difference is in the riders: that of the Waddesdon piece is not embellished with gems and the enameling of details in the costume, especially the helmet, is less accomplished than in the Gutman example.

The identity of the cartouches in the two examples, however, is especially striking, particularly in view of the promiscuity with which—in many other examples of jewels which might be cited—such parts have been altered or replaced. The British Museum dating is too broad, and granted that both cartouches and pendants are coeval, the other features of style and quality opt for South German, late 16th century.

An interesting analogue to the horse and rider image is provided by a St. George on horseback on the cover of an enameled gold watch formerly in the Carl Marfels Collection, Berlin, designed by N. Vallin, and dated by Forrer (1905, p. 27 and fig. 150 a & b) "about 1600." Vallin was watch-maker of Lyon (?) and this piece, patently made for English use, provides a striking index to the international complexities of the jewelry business of the time.

48 Pendant Heliotrope Whistle in Gold, Enamel, Jewels and Pearls: St. Hubert and the Stag

SOUTH GERMAN   CA. 1600 (?)

The pendant is suspended by two long chains left and right, and one short chain center, from a lobed cartouche surmounted by a single ring. The cartouche is enameled in opaque light blue, lavender, white and dark blue, and translucent red, green and blue. In the center of the cartouche, mounted in a high rectangular collet, is a table-cut ruby. The two long chains are attached right and left to the top and bottom collars of the heliotrope whistle. Each contain two four-lobed cartouches in light opaque blue and lavender, and translucent blue enamel with a table-cut emerald in gold collet in the center. Between these cartouches, in each chain, is a single pearl. The shorter chain, in the center, is attached at the bottom to the top of the cross between the stag's antlers. The basis of the composition is an octagonal, crescent-shaped, polished, heliotrope whistle. The larger end to the left, the smaller end with mouthpiece to the right. Centered within the concave portion of the crescent and held in place by five equally spaced collars around the whistle, is an elaborate, decorative, figurative composition of St. Hubert and the Stag. On the right, the Saint, clad in shirt, jerkin and hose of translucent green, blue and plum colored enamel respectively with flesh parts in opaque white and shoes in opaque blue enamel, crouches with his right hand on his chest and his left outstretched, holding his plumed cap of opaque white and translucent red enamel. His hair, borders of the costume, belt and hunting horn at his side are all in gold. The stag, with a cross of five table-cut diamonds and one rose-cut diamond in the center between his antlers, stands, head turned to right, upon a broken composition of mounted gems and enamel volutes, rosettes and borders. The stag's body, with the exception of the wound at the throat and a few abraded portions, is consistently enameled in opaque light gray. The antlers, eyes, interior of ears and muzzle are all in gold and opaque black. The central composition focuses upon a rectangular table-cut ruby, set in a high pyramidal mount enameled on the four sides with opaque blue and black arabesques above concave gold moldings separated by a thin, flat band of translucent red. At left, right and at the top of the central pyramid in smaller pyramidal mounts, also enameled opaque blue and black, are three table-cut diamonds. To right and left, attached to the two larger side table-cut diamonds by oval baluster mounts, two cabochon sapphires. Surrounding these stones and their mounts is an interlocking design of curled and stylized foliage in translucent green and blue, and opaque blue, green and black enamel. Beneath the central mount, a rosette of six petals in opaque blue and lavender, and translucent red enamel. To the left, running up the ascending horn of the crescent, the hound, in opaque blue and black enamel, turns his head back toward the stag in the center. This composition is attached to the heliotrope crescent by means of five equally spaced collars diminishing in size from the larger to the smaller ends of the whistle. The largest collar has a flat end surface enameled with arabesques in opaque blue and black, and translucent red, blue and green. The large, center band of the collar is opaque white enamel with gold arabesques and supports a rectangular, collet-mounted, table-cut ruby. The fringe is of opaque green enamel fleurs-de-lis. Toward the right the second collar of opaque white enamel between gold ropes supports a similarly mounted and cut ruby and contains, at the bottom, a ring from which is suspended, by a fluted conical pin mount, a baroque pearl. The third (central) collar at the axis of the composition is identical with the last mentioned, but bears a collet-mounted, table-cut diamond and has depending from it a scrolled cartouche

131

enameled opaque blue, lavender, light green, black and white, and translucent blue, red, green and plum. From the bottom of the cartouche is suspended another, similarly mounted, baroque pearl. The fourth collar, though smaller than the second one, is of the same type, with ruby and pendant pearl, while the fifth one terminates in the flaming gold mouthpiece of the whistle. Reverse: the figural adjuncts (St. Hubert, the stag and the hound) are fully modeled in the round and equally exquisite from behind. The gold backs of the mounted jewels and arabesques of the central part of the composition are masked from behind by a second open-work gold and enamel screen attached to the front by seven rivets and minimal necessary soldering at the interlaced parts. This back screen is enameled in opaque white, black, lavender, green and blue, and translucent blue, red and green.

Height overall from stationary loop through drop pearl 6⅛ (15.5)
Width at widest point 3³⁄₁₆ (8.1)
Published
    D'Otrange (1953) p. 132, ill. p. 129
BMA L.62.15.52
Gutman 1191

    This beautifully preserved piece, of such resplendent craftsmanship, is so consequential both as a monument and as to its style that it must be accounted for with a maximum of imagination and prudence. It poses, from any view, so much that is at once tempting and intimidating that the greatest latitude must be utilized to explain its existence. It presents problems which are technical, iconographic and stylistic.

    As a structure, the work is of interlocked strata of cast and carved gold plates, with gems and figures fused and riveted together, fabricated as an intricate, three dimensional whole. It relates in technique most clearly to German pendants of between 1590 and 1610, especially the back of the Waddesdon Bequest pendant in the British Museum (W. B. no. 148). In this, and most other of these pendants, the fastenings are bolts rather than rivets. The major jewels on the obverse are most often bolted, probably for easy and quick (emergency?) removal. In these also the fastenings are left clearly visible, as if the maker were re-asserting the elements of his craft. In the Gutman pendant all rivets have been burnished off at some time and the fastening of the principal center stone is inaccessible behind the enamel boss.

    Iconographically, the figure is surely St. Hubert and not his hagiographic alternative, St. Eustace. The latter, a captain of the guards under the Emperor Trojan, is represented in military dress facing the cross-crowned stag. A pendant whistle formerly in the Spitzer Collection (Spitzer Sale [1893] ill. pl. XLVII, no. 1858) shows the helmeted and kilted figure pointing a gun and kneeling to left on the curve of the whistle. The Aquitanian nobleman, Hubert, who encountered the cross-crowned stag in the Ardennes during Holy Week, carries the hunting-horn as an attribute and, as patron saint of dogs, is here fitly accompanied.

    It is with respect to the subtler and arguable matters of style and chronology that the piece is most intriguing. The number and excellence of the gems, the purity and mass of the gold, and the number of craft processes involved presume a major workshop and a flourishing (court?) patronage of primarily Catholic conviction. Of the European capitals which come to mind first, Munich during the reign of Albert V or Prague from the Emperor Rudolf II's accession in 1576 to about 1597 are initially attractive.

    The works produced for the Munich court, now in the Schatzkammer of the Residenz,

133

especially those of Master Hans Reimer and the Hausaltar of Albert V, display the frequent use of truncated pyramidal mounts combined with interlocking scroll and strap-work and human figures (Thoma and Hege [1955] pls. 37–42). There is the same keen-eyed realism combined with sumptuousness. But in the figures there is an attenuation, a manneristic swank and a South German taste for pseudo-classical costume which does not occur in the Gutman piece. Further, those South German pendants alluded to above, especially those in the Collaert-Mignon manner, separate obverse and reverse into two distinct composi-tions: it is quite impossible to infer the structure of either front or back from its other face. The Gutman piece is almost a three-dimensional entity, meant to be revolved, or revolved around, with its curved units leading the eye into the back and front. The figure of St. Hubert is not so much mannerist as romantic: the theatrical obeisance of St. Hubert recalls the ballet.

The works produced in Rudolphian Prague are so tentatively assigned that to cite this piece as one of them would be too hypothetical.

A provenance in Augsburg is still another permissable speculation, particularly if the non-figurative design is compared with that of a pendant formerly in the possession of the gallery À La Vielle Russie, New York (Hackenbroch [1954] pl. 93). Yet here also the mannerist, classically clothed and un-clothed figures of Orpheus and Eurydice are cut off from the back of the whole by a pierced framework.

St. Hubert's costume, consisting of close-fitting soft shoes, long hose and doublet with padded *mahaîtres*, is essentially early 14th century, of about 1430-1440. (Compare the figures in the Franco-Flem-ish, Arras or Tournai tapestry of courtiers with roses, in the Metropolitan Museum of Art.) Yet even here no striking parallels can be adduced. The shoes are blunt-toed and of ankle height, not the above-the-ankle, pointed type favored at this time. The figure's coiffure is neither that shaved to a level well above the ears (cf. those in the *Chronicles of Hainault* by Jean Wankelin, 1447–1450 [Brussels, Bibl. Roy. ms. 9242-4] nor the heavy combed locks falling over the forehead and fluffed at the nape of the neck of Italian fashion.

This jewel has a non-figurative center construction akin to South German, Munich or Augs-burg court workmanship of ca. 1570–1610, but not exactly like either in technique or style.

This, then, is the analysis of the piece as it can be made according to orthodox and extant evi-dence. In the study of jewels we are limited, as nowhere else, by the destruction and loss which have left to us only a pittance out of what was once an opulent treasury. The comparative-analogical method is thus faulted by the very reduction of examples: the absence of an extant parallel cannot be taken as the absence of all parallels. We are, therefore, constrained to interpret possibilities rather than expound certainties. Of these, there seems to be a choice between two, those of anticipation and atavism.

If we take the St. Hubert figure as *terminus a quo*, the provenance may be in the richest, and artistically the most skillful, circle in 15th century Europe, the Franco-Burgundian, most particularly during the reign of Philip the Good (1396–1467). Technically, only the enamelers of such phenomena as the "Goldenen Rössl" of 1403, the Widener Morse and the Langenburg necklace (Steingräber [1956] figs. 92–93) would be equal to the techniques of the Gutman pendant. The three-dimensionality of the saint, dog and stag could be ascribed to the modeling *en rond bosse*, with a gold core covered with multi-colored fluxes, practiced by the enamelers of Paris from the end of the 14th century forward. The realism, so evident in the face of St. Hubert, is evident also in the Widener Morse, and in the kneeling figures of King Charles VI and his Marshall before the madonna of the "Goldenen Rössl."

134

The use of St. Hubert rather than St. Eustace could be taken as some confirmation of a Franco-Burgundian provenance, inasmuch as the saint was Bishop of Liège when he died in 727.

The central jeweled construction, unmatched in surviving Burgundian pieces of this date, could only be accounted for by assuming that a master capable of perfecting so original and gorgeous a piece could also be capable of inventing motifs not commonplace until a century and a half later. That these motifs do not in all respects prefigure their later parallels might also be additional evidence for their independent origin.

Conversely, if the central portion of the whistle and the mounts of the jewels are taken as *terminus a quo*, and the piece is moved to South Germany, 1570–1610, the anachronistic human figure must be cited as a deliberate revival, or archaeological predilection on the maker's part. Such reoccurances are not unknown: the Duke of Burgundy's famous marten skin with ruby eyes, a diamond muzzle and teeth and nails of gold (cf., Tesier, "Dictionnaire d'Orfevrerie" in Migne, *Encyclopedia Théologique*, Vol. XXVII, "Collier de fourrure") of 1467 appears again in the design of Hans Muelich for a similarly mounted fur of 1550 in the Bayerisches National Museum (Steingräber [1956] fig. 219) nor is atavism uncommon in other fields at this and other times.

Mrs. Eric Newton, of the Courtauld Institute of the University of London, is of the opinion that the whistle is an insignia of the Order of St. Hubert, founded by Gerhard of Ravensberg in 1444, an early version of which may be seen in the arms of Jülich and Berg in the *Wappenbuch* of Conrad Grünenberg (facsimile edition 1875). Mrs. Newton's proposed publication of the piece is awaited with impatience, for it occurs to the cataloguer that if the objections that can be made ungallantly in advance are met, she will have untangled a problem with great adroitness. According to Perrot (1820, p. 57 and pl. XIV) "cet ordre cessa entièrement d'exister depuis 1489 jusqu'en 1709, époque ou l'électeur palatin Jean-Guillaume de Neubourg, duc de Juliers, le retablit." J. H. Lawrence-Archer (1887, pp. 33 ff.) states that the order fell into abeyance in 1609, when the male line of the House of Liège failed. It was reconstituted on September 29, 1708, by the Elector Palatine John William of Neuburg. Maximilian Joseph I, first King of Bavaria, enlarged the statues on the 19th of May, 1808, making it the first order of the kingdom. As reconstituted, the badge, collar and star illustrated by Lawrence-Archer have nothing in common with the whistle in question. Von Biedenfeld (1841, 11, p. 119) cites the earlier form of the order as "eine Art Medaille, später aber ein anderes grünfarbenes Abzeichen in Form einer Birne, worauf die Legende des heiligen Hubert in Gold abgebildet, und woran mit goldenen Schnüren ein Hüfthorn gleichfals von Gold befestiget gewesen." The chain in this case consists of 42 links with 21 panels representing the encounter of St. Hubert and the stag, St. Hubert kneeling and accompanied by dog and servant, and therefore it can be clear that the Gutman whistle is not to be identified with the order as described by von Biedenfeld. And, of course, the Gutman whistle is assuredly not pear-shaped. In Schoonebeek (1697, no. LXXXVIII, pl. 88) a knight of the order is illustrated wearing an elliptical pendant.

The question is not whether the whistle appertains to the Order of St. Hubert, but what its date is and under what circumstances it could have been made. It does not conform to any of the prescriptions of the insignia, and its combination of romanticism and late-Renaissance eclecticism is out of the ordinary. On the other hand, jewels of about 1600 are of the most curious and variegated shapes. St. Hubert, though customarily kneeling, can assume the wildest postures, as in an anonymous mannerist work in the Church of St. Leonhard, Léau, Brabant (illustrated in *Aesculape*, 28me Année [NS] nos. 7 and 8, July–August 1938, p. 194). Here the invention is so unconventional as to make any reservations about the Gutman piece seem niggling.

No explanation is wholly satisfactory, yet in view of our woeful insecurity in the field, no invidious doctrinaire judgments should be passed. In any case, this whistle remains as spectacular a one as is to be found in any collection today, and certainly the finest of its kind in America today.

Pendant Ship with Two Figures in Gold, Enamel, Pearls and Jewels

ITALIAN (POSSIBLY SPANISH OR DANISH ?)   LATE 16TH CENTURY   *Color plate, frontispiece*

From two plain gold links hangs a cast, carved and punch-tooled cartouche of interlocking volutes with a central, five-petaled rosette and side crown bosses enameled opaque light blue, dark blue and white, and translucent red and dark blue. From the cartouche depend two chains, plain links of which are connected by small, square, table-cut rubies in collet mounts flanked by single seed pearls. To these chains the pendant proper is attached, which consists of a single-masted vessel containing two figures. The mast, center, is enameled opaque blue and topped by a gold sphere through which run four twisted gold stays. Seated to left and right in bow and stern, respectively, a female figure in cap, ruff, stomacher and puffed sleeves, enameled opaque white and translucent blue, and a male figure with conical carnival cap, ruff, doublet, trunks and slashed sleeves, enameled opaque green, light blue and black. The interior, or deck, of the vessel is enameled opaque and translucent blue. Around the exterior of the bulwarks, obverse, are two rows of collet-mounted, table-cut rubies, five in the prow and eight in the stern. The three-tiered body of the ship is enameled with opaque blue and green arabesques on a background of opaque black and carries, center, a square, table-cut, collet-mounted yellow topaz. The rudder and keel are enameled translucent red and opaque white. A second openwork, lobed-cartouche terminates the pendant. It is enameled translucent red and green and is centered

137

by a table-cut, collet-mounted dusky green beryl or tourmaline surrounded by eighteen opaque white enameled petals and ending in a single pendant pin-fastened baroque pearl. On the reverse the upper cartouche is enameled opaque white, blue, green and black. The backs of the two figures are enameled opaque blue with gold crosses; the gunwales are decorated with shields of translucent green blue and red; the body of the ship is four-tiered with opaque light blue and green oval panels in opaque black, and a bottom cartouche with an adjacent sunburst enameled opaque dark and light blue, white, black and green. The vessel is cast and carved in two halves, fused along the keel and center of the deck. Fronts of figures and port deck are hollow cast and carved and fused with separate backs on the starboard deck. The rudder, keel and bottom cartouche are separately cast, carved and fused. The gems on the body of the vessel apparently are bolted or riveted on the inside.

Height overall 2¹³⁄₁₆ (7.2)
Height from top of mast through pearl drop 2³⁄₁₆ (5.6)
Width 1¹¹⁄₁₆ (4.3)
Collections
   Madame de X
   Baron Max von Goldschmidt-Rothschild
Exhibited
   Art Institute of Chicago (1951–1962) RX200/71
Published
   Madame de X Sale (1912) no. 6, ill.
   Goldschmidt-Rothschild Sale (1950) II, p. 24, no. 94, ill. p. 23
   D'Otrange (1952) p. 66, ill.
   Hackenbroch (1954) pp. 168–172, ill. pl. 94F
BMA L.62.15.138
Gutman 1144

A provenance for this charming piece is not given in the first sale catalogue of 1912. It becomes "Spanish, Early 17th century" in the Goldschmidt-Rothschild Sale (1950); D'Otrange (1952) publishes it as "Italian 16th century." Hackenbroch (1954) calls it "Italian or Spanish, late 16th century" but recently (Hackenbroch [1965] pp. 200–205, fig. 7) she attributes it, among others, to the Trentine goldsmith Giovanni Battista Scolari who worked in Munich for Duke William IV between 1567 and 1582, an ascription examined in detail below.

   Ship pendants, also known as "nef" or "navette" pendants began to appear as soon as the age of maritime exploration had caught the fancy of craftsmen. Mary of Burgundy, daughter of Charles the Bold, had *une petite nef d'or, estoffée de tout son appareil* ("a small ship of gold loaded with all its gear." For this reference to her inventory in Lille see Smith [1909] p. 246, fn. 1). As early as 1519, Henry VIII of England had a diamond and pearl ship pendant (Brewer [1867] III, p. 164). Queen Elizabeth had several; one was "a jeuel of golde, being a shippe, sett with a table dyamonde, of fyve sparcks of dyamondes and a smale perle pendaunte . . ." (quoted by Smith [1909] p. 253) and one, now in Berkeley Castle, is said to have been given the Queen by Sir Francis Drake. This has an ebony hull, enameled gold rigging and a dinghy hanging below.

138

The place of origin for the majority of these pendants has been given as probably the Adriatic area, on the basis of an analogy between them and specimens of jewels from the Greek Islands in the Franks Bequest in the British Museum (Smith [1909] p. 246). If this is true it would, of course, make Venice the principal putative point of origin. The type of vessel is much the same throughout: one or more masts, high forecastle and poop, rigging of twisted gold wire, and brightly enameled hull of both translucent and opaque enamels (cf. no. 50).

While it would be safest to follow such precedent and assign the piece to Venice, at the end of the 16th century, there are aspects of it which make an alternative—if speculative—designation attractive.

Yvonne Hackenbroch, in her recent article (1965), has grouped the Gutman pendant together with five others portraying figures in gondolas or barques (one in the collection of Mr. and Mrs. Jack Linsky, one at Waddesdon Manor, two in the Palazzo Pitti and one at Schloss Rosenborg) and given them to Giovanni Battista Scolari. The essential part of her captivating and somewhat involved thesis is that Scolari, a Trentine goldsmith mentioned in the court accounts between 1567 and 1583, having, as Zanne, taken part (along with Orlando di Lasso) in an Italian comedy during the celebration of the marriage of Duke William to Renata of Lorraine, commemorated his success in a jewel now in the Museo degli Argenti of the Palazzo Pitti, Florence. She then utilizes the other five, including the Gutman pendant, to form an opus. Unfortunately no concrete evidence is adduced to connect Scolari with the pieces, and there is no consistent stylistic relation between any of them.

Of the great expansive maritime powers of the late 16th century there were four: Spain, England, Venice and Denmark. The piece is so gaily secular that a Spanish origin is difficult to imagine. Yet Diego Vazquez of Toledo was paid twenty reals for "repairing a navette" on January 3, 1539 (Cathedral Archives, quoted in Davillier [1879] p. 199). The technique of the enamel practically forbids its being English. It does not have the elaboration one associates with Venice (cf., Evans [1953] pl. 83). Though to do so is to invite for himself the challenge just made, the cataloguer suggests, and does not adumbrate as fact, the possibility of Denmark, late in the reign of Frederick II (1559–1588) or early in the reign of Christian IV (1588–1648). Yvonne Hackenbroch's point that Venetian themes exercised a powerful romantic influence on the north could apply just as well here. Christian IV was responsible for the foundation of both a militant and commercial navy capable of offsetting the power of Sweden and the Hanseatic cities; as ports he founded Glückstadt and Christianhavn. He employed the Bavarian Corvianus Saur as court goldsmith as well as indigenes of extraordinary talent such as Didrik Fiuren, who made his crown.

Details of the piece are somewhat composite—displaced and reassembled. The costume of the female could be Italianate-Spanish of about 1580 (cf., the portrait of Quintilia Fischieri by F. Baroccio, National Gallery of Art, Washington). That of the male appears to be some sort of carnival garb, again possibly Venetian. But the enamel patterns on the hull are analogous to those of many international designers working between 1600 and 1615. The provenance "Italian, but perhaps Danish or possibly even Spanish" may be resolved in favor of one of these countries by further study. For the moment the Italian attribution will be the most popular. The piece is no less splendid for these questions, but the more interesting.

139

50   Pendant in Gold, Enamel and Pearls: A Ship in Full Sail

VENICE (?) OR SPAIN (?)   CA. 1600 (?)

The pendant is suspended by two chains from a lobed cartouche of translucent red enamel containing a center piece of three heart-shaped leaves enameled opaque blue and white, three elongated opaque green leaves and a trefoil opaque white center piece. The two chains, the shorter of which is attached to the bowsprit, the longer to the poop, are composed of flat and twisted links and each chain is punctuated by three seed pearls. The vessel has a main mast, foremast and five sails (six including that held by Fortune, see below). The main mast is a tapering gold cylinder provided with crow's nest and rigging of corded gold rope which is attached to the open rails (?); the smaller foremast is also provided with similar rigging. The main mast is topped by a moveable gold pennant. Both masts are topped by opaque blue enamel beads. The sails are opaque white enamel on bent sheets of punctured gold. Part of the rigging of the foremast is twisted around the bowsprit, also a tapered gold cylinder. Focs'le and after cabin are enameled with dots, pointed ovals and bands of opaque green, turquoise blue, dark blue and white. Atop the after cabin is a standing figure of Fortune? (Victory?) in opaque white enamel holding the top of the sail in her right hand and the fluttering end in her left. Her left foot is missing. On the main deck and poop are three tiny figures, the forward figure enameled translucent green, the remaining two translucent red. The hull, with voluted gunnels of translucent red enamel, is covered in an opaque white scale pattern, above translucent green enamel leaves. There is a large circular central rosette of five heart-shaped opaque blue and white enamel leaves, five elongated opaque green leaves and a center, five-leaved rosette of translucent red enamel. Three pendant pearls are suspended from the keel, the center pearl has a baluster mount with translucent red enamel droplets.

Height to top of cartouche 4 (10.2)
Length of ship 2%6 (6.5)
Collection
    Frederic Spitzer
Exhibited
    Detroit Institute of Arts (1958–1959)
Published
    Bonnaffé (1891) III, p. 148, no. 35
    Spitzer Sale (1893) II, p. 47, ill. pl. XLVI, no. 1820
    Detroit (1958) pp. 146–147, no. 373, ill. p. 149
BMA L.62.15.223
Gutman 889

Much that could be said about this second *nef* has already been adduced in regard to no. 49. This present one, though more representative, is not without a nodus or two of its own. It came from the Spitzer Collection and is illustrated in the Spitzer Sale catalogue (1893) pl. XLVII, no. 1820. An almost identical companion from the same collection (*ibid.*, pl. XLVII, no. 1846) is now in the Victoria and Albert Museum and is labeled Venetian, late 16th century (Victoria and Albert Inventory of Art Objects [1893] p. 97, no. 696–1893, "Italian, 16th Century"; also Evans [1953] pl. 83b as "probably Venetian"). A third

example is in the Louvre (Steingräber [1956] fig. 199, "Venedig, um 1600") and a fourth in the Grassi Collection (Grassi Sale [1927] p. 172, no. 463, ill. p. 173, as "Flemish (?) XVI Century").

Kertesz (1947, p. 452) reproduces a drawing for such a pendant ship which, on p. 449, he cites as reproduced from Davallier (1879). The drawing is clearly one made *after* the Victoria and Albert example, for its materials are described, yet the location is given as Barcelona. This is either a typographical error (as seems most likely) or, if the drawing does reproduce one of the 16th century Barcelona mastercraftsman's probationary drawings, the Victoria and Albert example must represent its finished examplar.

The cataloguer has handled the Victoria and Albert ship and can vouch for its resemblance to the Gutman pendant. Both are hollow and made basically from two halves joined by interior flat hook-and-eye clips fastened, apparently, before the addition of the superstructure. Both pieces (and it is to be assumed, the Louvre example as well) are characterized by a curiously metallic resonance, as if the medium were highly alloyed. In this respect they resemble the products of a commercial enterprise rather than specially designed items from a craftsman's atelier. This confusing evidence, as yet unresolved, begs the choice between Spain and Venice. It is this cataloguer's opinion that these matters of provenance and date must remain conjectural, and further studies instituted. These may afford only further conjecture, but hopefully they will lead to plausible solutions to vexing problems.

142

51   Diamond Shaped Pendant of Gold, Enamel and Jewels with
      Enameled Figures

SOUTH GERMAN   LATE 16TH CENTURY

The diamond shaped pendant is suspended from a single cast ring at the apex. The fabric is tripartite: technical and constituent description must go hand in hand. Part one is a composition of cast and carved open-work interlocked scrolls. Above, two putti facing outward sit to left and right, and below, two hippocamps facing inward are to left and right. Two tiny *mascarons* are at the top and bottom. Symmetrically placed left and right, top and bottom, are four rectangular table-cut diamonds in pyramidal collet mounts. This fabric bears remnants of opaque white, black and blue, and translucent green enamel. Part two is a circular separate band of ten rectangular table-cut rubies in collet mounts reinforced at the corners by abutments. Part three consists of the center circular scrolled wreath enameled opaque white, black and light green, and translucent red, with a rectangular table-cut pyramidal collet-mounted diamond at the hub. The ornate and ruggedly gorgeous effect to the piece is due primarily to loss of enamel. Part one, the containing fabric, was wax cast and left almost unrefined: all rough gold parts must be imagined as enameled. Part two, the circular band of rubies, is smoothly burnished and backed by a circular gold plate fastened by four rivets. Part three, the interior wreath holding the central diamond, is inserted from the front and is fastened through the gold plate of part two by three bolts which hold in position a gold bar, which in turn acts as reinforcement and also as the base of the diamonds left and right. The diamonds at top and bottom are fastened separately by bolts through reinforcing gold bars. A pendant pin-fastened pearl hangs at the bottom.

Height 2¹¹⁄₁₆ (6.8)
Width 2⅛ (5.4)
Collection
    Baron Nathaniel von Rothschild
Exhibited
    Detroit Institute of Arts (1958–1959)
Published
    Detroit (1958) p. 147, no. 371, ill. p. 148
BMA L.62.15.63
Gutman 1200

The indisputable splendor of this piece makes the issue of date and provenance a critical one. Both Mr. Gutman and the Detroit Institute of Arts have considered it to be Italian, 16th century, probably second quarter, by reason of an affinity with a pendant formerly in the collections of Cardinal Albergati and Professor Luigi Grassi (Grassi Sale [1927] p. 185, no. 487). Professor Pietro Toesca, who is responsible for the expertise of the jewelry in the Grassi catalogue, speaks of the Albergati-Grassi pendant as belonging "to Florentine art of the epoch of Benvenuto Cellini, whose influence is clearly discerned in the capricious ornateness and refined execution of the piece," a somewhat reckless pronouncement. A pendant of similar

143

shape and with analogous disposition of jewels was in the Eugen Gutman Collection (von Falke [1912] p. 13 no. 32, ill. pl. 10) and was called "South German, probably Augsburg, end of the 16th Century."

Although combinations of putti, heavily carved whorls, hippocamps and *mascarons* are so internationally disposed that a provenance more exact than "South German, or North Italian, end of the 16th century," might seem to be inadvisable, nonetheless, something of the rich grandeur of this piece suggests the work of the great Hans Muelich, and a comparison with this extant design for a necklace of the Four Elements and Twelve Signs of the Zodiac confirms this nexus. (Basserman-Jordan [1909] fig. 127.)

144

52 Necklace in Gold, Enamel, Pearls and Jewels

SCOTLAND (?)   SECOND HALF OF THE 16TH CENTURY   *Color plate facing page 122*

The necklace consists of twenty links and a pendant. The links are of three different types .Type 1, of ten links: these consist of squares containing four seed pearls in the corners, four collet-mounted,table-cut rubies arranged as a lozenge around a collet-mounted, table-cut diamond, and four droplets of opaque light blue enamel. The sustaining frame bears traces of opaque dark blue enamel. Two of these squares serve as sockets for the flange clasp which permits the separation of the necklace into two equal bracelets. Type 2, of five links: these are figure-of-eight knots embellished with small table-cut rubies and two two-holed bridges of opaque white enamel. Type 3, of five links: these consist of two ad-dorsed crescents, embellished with table-cut rubies and containing, within the horns and center, two table-cut rubies and four droplets of opaque blue enamel. The crescents are reinforced by tri-lobed bridges of opaque white enamel. All of the links are connected by simple gold rings and are consistently enameled with deep blue translucent enamel. The pendant is a monogram of the initials F and B, combined with an anchor beneath a coronet canopy, the whole studded with table-cut rubies. The reverse of the pendant has opaque white and translucent red, blue and green enamel with the inscription on the stock of the anchor, "HOVP . FEIDIS . ME." Beneath the anchor, a pendant Siamese pearl.

Height from upper medallion through drop pearl 2¼ (5.7)
Width of medallion ¹⁵⁄₁₆ (2.4)
Length of necklace, omitting metal clasp insert 17⅜ (44.2)
Length of bracelet section with medallion attached 8½ (21.7)
Length of second bracelet without medallion 8 ¹¹⁄₁₆ (22.1)
Width of chain ½ (1.3)
Collections
   S. J. Phillips, London
   R. W. M. Walker
Exhibited
   Glasgow (1898)
   Walters Art Gallery (1948)
   Art Institute of Chicago (1951–1962) RX 200/27
Published
   D'Otrange (1952) p. 69, ill. p. 71
BMA L. 62.15.96
Gutman 948

D'Otrange, the collector and the Art Institute of Chicago are agreed in assigning the piece to Scotland, third quarter of the 16th century. Though acceptable as a provenance, in view of the absence of any unmistakable evidence to the contrary, the piece is not lacking in imponderables.

   A pendant formed of a monogram and anchor is most exceptional, and the coronet above the

anchor appears to conform to no special type, and may be only a decorative motif. The motto, "HOVP FEIDIS ME," is even more inscrutable. It can be taken as some dialectical variation of "Hope [is] my faith" (ME. *feith* or OFr. *feid*) or "Hope feedeth me." Extensive correspondence with heraldic and genealogical authorities in Great Britain has produced no recorded instance of the motto being an epigraph appropriate to a particular family. The combination of the "love-knots," anchor, monogram and motto would posit that we have here a betrothal or marriage gift made for a single couple, the coronet being an allusion to that part of the feminine costume.

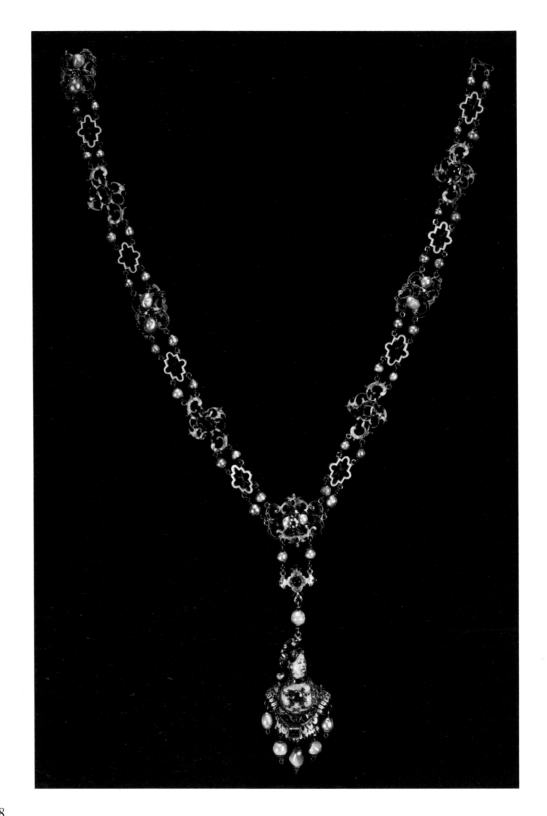

53 Necklace of Gold, Enamel, Pearls and Jewels with a Pendant Bust of Minerva

NORTH ITALIAN AND SOUTH GERMAN   CA. 1580 AND CA. 1613

The necklace consists of three separate types of links. Three links and the bottom cartouche are of type A consisting of a cast and carved SS design of opaque black enamel bands upon interlocked gold reverse S's partially enameled opaque white. In the center a quatrefoil rosette enameled translucent red and green, and opaque white, flanked by volutes of opaque blue and white. This separate member, riveted to the base through the center, supports two pin-fastened pearls. The bottom cartouche consists of symmetrically interlocked curving bands enameled black with a reserve gold pattern of alternate bead and reel. A central vertical axial ornament in pipe-tooled gold is ornamented at the center with a red and white enameled rosette flanked by two pearls, and the axis terminates at top and bottom in gold C scrolls ornamented and linked to the rosette with enameled foliation in opaque blue and white, and translucent red. Four links are of type B. Each link is composed of three parts: the base, a center rosette, and a collet-mounted ruby. The base is a cast and carved symmetrical design of two volutes and two arabesques, both enameled opaque white with beads of translucent red. The center rosette is an oval with eight projecting arms in opaque white with droplets of opaque blue. On top of a cylindrical base, fastened through the base design by a bolt, is a rectangular, high collet-mounted, table-cut ruby. Eight links are of type C and each consists of a rectangular frame of opaque white enamel with quatrefoils and six droplets of translucent red. The interior corners are connected by transverse, slightly raised bands of translucent red, centered with translucent green bead. There are four rings at each corner and the enameling is identical on the obverse and reverse. All these links are connected by twin pearls capped by translucent red rosettes. Below the bottom cartouche is a second, smaller cartouche basically a four-petaled flower with a translucent red center and three droplets, top and bottom, of translucent red and opaque blue. The bust of Minerva is suspended from a riveted ring emerging from the crest of her helmet. The bust, hollow-cast in three-quarter profile, looks to the right. She wears a crested helmet enameled opaque white (crest) and translucent blue, with a grotesque visor of opaque aubergine. On the side of the helmet is a triangular, rose-cut diamond in a circular scalloped and *tête-de-clou* mount. Flesh parts of the bust are of opaque white enamel. The gorget consists of a table-cut ruby flanked by two small marquise diamonds. The shoulder pieces of the armor are grotesque masks of opaque aubergine; the body of the armor is opaque green with gold arabesques spotted with translucent blue curling over the clavicles and breasts, supporting a rose-cut ruby in a high circular collet. The girdle is of three rose-cut diamonds and two table-cut rubies inserted from behind through slots in the casing. The lappets are of opaque white and translucent blue and green enamel with a rectangular, table-cut emerald in the center. From beneath the shoulder pieces and the apron depend five disk-capped pearls. The reverse of this pendant bust is masked by an incised shield, fitted into the profile, of a different color gold and totally different design. This is bolted to the bust with three square, foliated bolts, attached to the gorget, center ruby and girdle.

Length of necklace 18 (46)
Length of pendant 4 (10.2)

Exhibited
    Walters Art Gallery (1948)
    Art Institute of Chicago (1951–1962) RX200/14
Published
    D'Otrange (1952) p. 69, ill. p. 71
BMA L.62.15.84
Gutman 892

This piece is notoriously rich in study material, and since links of necklaces can be effortlessly combined, any piece comprising a combination of different types, as here, must be considered according to its components.

The four links and bottom cartouche on this necklace of type A, described above, with their punch-tooled obverse surfaces, are so international in style as to defy more than the most hypothetical placement in time and locality. The cataloguer suggests, in view of their sculpturesque presentation,

North Italy, about 1580. The four links of type B exert an entirely different effect. These are closely related to the flat, centrifugally active designs of Mignot and Carteron of the first two decades of the 17th century. A garment fastening of the same type is in the Austrian Museum of Applied Art, Vienna (Steingräber [1956] fig. 215); a parallel asymmetrical form and its use as dress-ornament are represented on the garment of Herzogin Magdalene von Neuburg, in a portrait by Pietro Candido (?) dated about 1613 (*ibid.*, fig. 171).

The eight links of type C appear to be the earliest, being akin to the strapwork utilized in reverses by Hans Mielich, ca. 1570. Finally, the bust of Minerva (of which the crudely fitted backing must be considered an undatable intrusion) can most probably be assigned to North Italy, about 1580, with its architectural insertion of square-cut stones beneath the bust.

Thus, the whole must be fragmented into the following: the necklace, North Italy about 1580, and South Germany about 1613; pendant, North Italy about 1580.

Necklace of Eighteen Filigree Links with Pearls

SPANISH (?)   17TH CENTURY

The necklace is composed of eighteen cast, reticulated links and two triangular end pieces. Each link consists of a partially open and partially hollow floriated pattern surrounding a central circle. At each corner and between each floriated pattern are hemispherical bosses. The "petals" of the design are filled with opaque green enamel and opaque white enamel painted red and black. Each central circle is filled with a shallow concave deposit of black and white enamel, probably originally without further decoration. This center has been roughly broken into and is now masked by a single pearl wired to the face by a gold wire twist-fastened in back of the link. On the reverse, each link has four rings through which run two twisted silk cords holding two pearls between each link. The triangular end pieces are cast and enameled in the same manner.

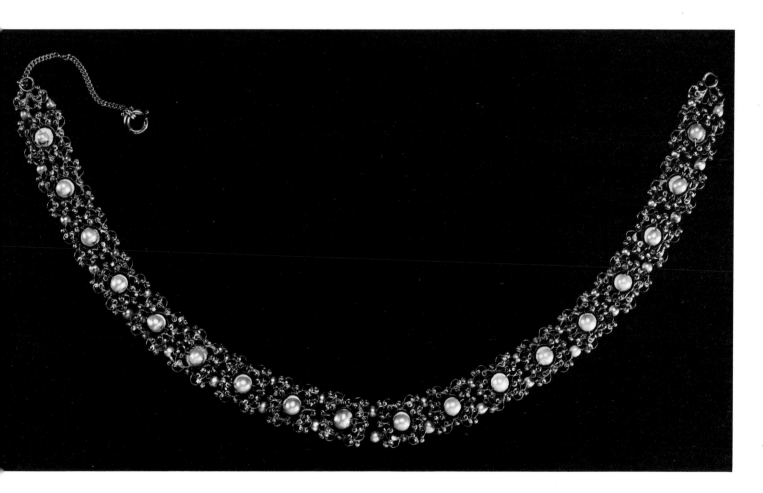

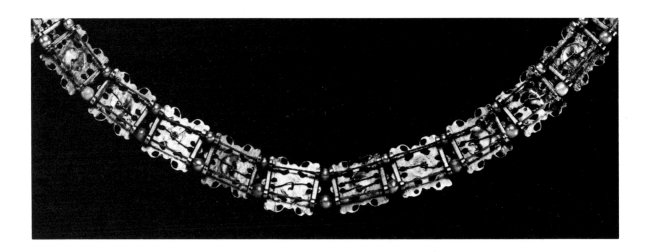

Length omitting metal ring clasp 11¾₆ (28.4)
Width ⁹⁄₁₆ (1.4)
Exhibited
   Art Institute of Chicago (1951–1962) RX200/37
Published
   D'Otrange (1952) pp. 69–70
BMA L.62.15.106
Gutman 982

With respect to this luxurious piece, Mr. Gutman, the Art Institute of Chicago and D'Otrange unite in the opinion that this piece is most probably Venetian, of about 1600 or early 17th-century, with the first two sources proposing a secondary Spanish origin.

As can be ascertained from the description above, the appearance of the piece as a necklace is now both more luxurious and more exotic than it might have presented in a pristine state. The links, some of which may be missing, are threaded on silk cords and separated by pearls, to be accepted only hesitantly as the original intention. The central disks of the links, now filled with pearls, must originally have been domed, opaque-enameled bosses. Lacking these, the problem of comparisons becomes very difficult, for only the metalwork itself has not been touched, and the original composition of the piece as a necklace is a matter that must remain open.

The composition of the links as an entwining of slender stalks ending in hemispherical pellets appears to be an essentially Spanish device; in the more elaborate intact pieces the foliations surround cut gems in conical collets (cf. Johnson [1944] p. 244, fig. 221) and the petals may be enameled, as here, in red, green or blue. Moorish filigree of the 12th and 13th centuries was revived in the 17th century, at first in Córdoba and Salamanca, then in other centers (*ibid.*, p. 110); the technique here resembles a consolidation of the filigree strands into a sculpturesque baroque density.

55   Enameled Gold Necklace with Rubies

HUNGARIAN (?)   17TH CENTURY

The necklace is composed of twenty-six large links and twenty-three smaller, connecting links. Each large link consists of a cast gold bed in the shape of a fleur-de-lis of three ostrich feathers set face to face and filled with opaque white and black enamel. On the reverse these links are enameled opaque turquoise blue. Riveted through the center of each is an oval, gold, collet mount containing a table-cut ruby. Each link is connected to its fellow by a bent gold band, fused to the top of which is the smaller link, a long, oval, collet mount containing two small rectangular table-cut rubies. Three of these smaller ruby links are missing and are replaced by plain gold bands.

Length 14¼ (36.2)
Width ⁹⁄₁₆ (1.5)
Collections
    Baron Herzog M. Lipot
    Martin Desmoni
Exhibited
    Hungarian Museum of Art (1931)

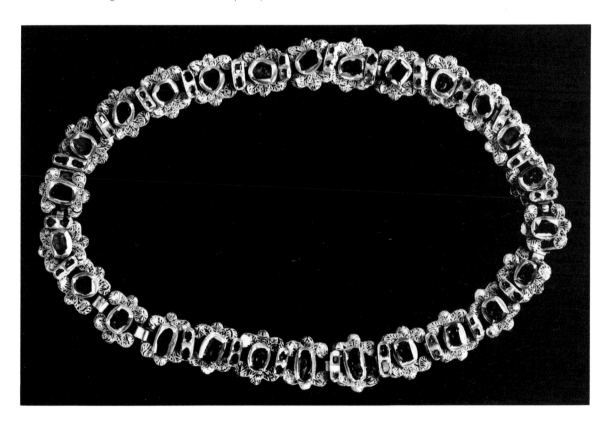

Published
  Desmoni Sale (1958) p. 30, no. 86, ill. pl. 16
BMA L.62.15.68
Gutman 1431

This chain of links exhibits a vigor of design that is noteworthy. Both the collector and the Desmoni Sale catalogue offer the option of a French or Hungarian provenance. The cataloguer can in truth see no grounds for, nor find parallels to support, the French ascription, especially when combined with the late 16th century date suggested in the Desmoni catalogue.

The workmanship is at once broad yet elegant, as if the skillfully mounted stones had been combined with much less refined units. The blue enamel on the reverse is flecked and pitted; the gyves securing the larger links to the smaller are rugged and quite inferior to the faces of the links. Thus the Hungarian provenance—one which would be more likely to explain this inconsistency—seems preferable, but the possibility of some other place of origin cannot be ruled out. A typological parallel, admittedly not the closest, but typologically presentable, is afforded by bracelets in a portrait of Maria de Bije by M. Miereveld dated 1620 (Gans [1961] fig. 35). Indeed, the present chain is of such construction and length that it may well have once constituted two matching bracelets. The date could not be earlier than this, and probably is later.

 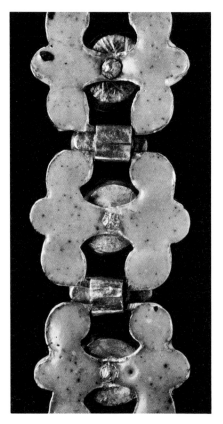

56 Necklace of Gold, Enamel, Jewels and Pearls

SOUTH GERMAN AND HUNGARIAN   CA.1600–1630 AND MID-17TH CENTURY

This elaborate piece consists of four parts: (A) two double cartouche links at either end; (B) twenty-four almost square open-work black and white enameled links, grouped in threes, the center link bearing a six-leaved black rosette with pearl; (C) six gold enameled and jeweled cartouche links (of the same design as the double cartouche at the end); (D) a large open-work rosette at mid-point. The two double cartouches (A) at the ends are made according to identical designs. A cast and carved bed of interlocking arabesques, enameled opaque black, white and blue, and translucent red, serves as the base for a high, square collet mount containing a table-cut ruby which is surrounded by a foliated second base, enameled opaque black and blue, and translucent red and green. These three pieces—the cartouche, the base of the collet and the collet itself, are riveted through the center of the cartouche. Lying between and joining these two cartouches is a four-leaved gold rosette with a center of translucent orange *basse-taille* enamel also heavily bolted to the reverse. Next in order to these double cartouche end links come trios of black and white enamel links (B) consisting of a nearly square frame centered with a six-leaved black rosette with opaque white enamel center. The second or center link or each triad has a raised and slightly concave rosette centered by a pearl. These triads are all connected by semi-circular gold links masked in front by five-petal rosettes analogous to the black and white center rosettes. Between every pair of such triads (B) is a single tri-partite cartouche (C) consisting of base, base of collet and collet with table-cut ruby, the whole corresponding to one cartouche of the double cartouche (A) already described. The center rosette (D) is a large spoked sectional ornament enameled opaque white and black, and translucent green, set with table-cut emeralds and table and rose-cut diamonds. This rosette consists of (1) an open-work base to which have been soldered arms or brackets which bear, at their ends, three part rosettes consisting of a sort of cross *Avellan* enameled opaque green and blue with four white flowers, each a four foliate; (2) a base enameled translucent green and opaque black; and (3) a square collet-mounted, table-cut emerald (one is rectangular). All three parts are riveted through the end of the arm. Superimposed on this rosette and held in place on a central axle is a separate arabesque sunburst enameled opaque black and white, and translucent green, with diamonds in collet mounts designed as leaves. A third, topmost and last section consists of a hexagonal collet mount in the center. Separately mounted to the bedplate on separate axles are four tripartite arabesques enameled opaque black and white, and translucent green, bearing collet-mounted, table-cut diamonds. All of these parts, except the bedplate itself, are separately moveable on their axis. On the reverse of the bedplate is an incised, black enameled inscription.

Length overall 24¹³⁄₁₆ (63)
Height of medallion 3⁷⁄₁₆ (8.8)
Width of medallion 3¹⁄₁₆ (7.8)
Width of links 1¼ (3.1)
Collection
    Baron Nathaniel von Rothschild
BMA L.62.15.69
Gutman 1242

Here again we have the exacting problem of the presumptive composite. Six single links and the double links at each end, with their typical truncated pyramidal mounts and interlaced scrolls, are probably South German, of about 1600–1630. (Cf. the jewel in the Victoria and Albert Museum, M. 447–1927, of enameled gold, set with diamonds, purchased under the Francis Reubell Bryan Bequest.) The remaining links and the rosette are of different style and workmanship.

Dr. Elemer Bako, Finno-Ugrian Area Librarian of the Library of Congress, offers a tentative suggestion for the interpretation of the inscription on the back of the rosette. The inscription appears to be of the following elements:

S M D K C L IV REX

Since the inscription is on the reverse, it more likely applies to the maker, rather than the owner. The elements M, D, C, L and IV, Dr. Bako further suggests, would provide the year, MDCLIV, 1654, whereas the letters S and K stand for the initials of the name of the maker. The remaining part, REX, at the end of the text, would appear to be an abbreviation of *aurifex* (goldsmith), a term which has been used in Hungary since the 15th century.

Dr. Bako believes that the monogram SK could be that of the goldsmith Simon Krikavinus, of Eperjes (now Pre᷉ov in Slovakia) mentioned in contemporary sources in 1664 (Köszeghy [1936] p. 103) and with a monogram, the letters of which seem to be similar to the characteristics of those inscribed on this jewel. The decade's difference between 1654 and 1664 is not grave.

A comparison afforded by a brooch in the Victoria and Albert Museum called by Steingräber (1956, fig. 246) "French or German, about 1630," in style very close to the rosette of the present necklace, suggests that both pieces should be called Hungarian, ca. 1654.

160

Necklace of Fifteen Links in Gold, Enamel, Diamonds and Pearls

ITALIAN   SECOND HALF OF THE 16TH CENTURY AND CA. 1620–1630

The necklace consists of a two-part clasp closing a chain which is made up of (A) eight large links, (B) seven small links, and (C) fourteen links consisting simply of collet-mounted, table-cut diamonds (twelve in silver and two in gold) linked between (A) and (B). Each large link (A) consists of a lozenge-shaped *ajouré* gold frame embellished with volutes, enameled opaque black, white and blue, and translucent green. The reverse of each (A) link is identical with the front. The frame and unenameled surfaces are lightly punch-tooled with a small convex punch. From the center rises a gold cylinder which acts as a support for the center of a group of three pearls held by gold wire. Curved bands of gold support the center and function as both decoration and reinforcement. Most of the interior and exterior volutes and bands have been separately soldered to the cast lozenge-shaped frame. The third link-type (C) is of table-cut diamonds, in high pyramidal facet mountings of silver, which connect the larger and smaller links, (A) and (B). The smaller (B) links are complex in structure and are developed on one side only (the reverse is a flat gold plate) and consist of an asymmetrical gold, heart-shaped frame with a foliate pattern, the ground enameled in opaque black. At one end of each (B) link is a long, triangular, rose-cut diamond in gold collet mount; in the center of each link is a table-cut diamond in high, pyramidal, gold facet bolted through the link and held by a nut on the reverse, and at the opposite end is a second, shorter, rose-cut, triangular diamond in triangular collet mount. Also at one end of each of these (B) links is a circular gold loop, its face enameled opaque black. The link at the other end is a silver flange inserted within a slot and held in place by a gold rivet reaching through to the base of the aforementioned long triangular diamond. The center, or midway, link of the whole is one of these smaller links (B) and has on its reverse a bent, wire hoop for the suspension of some additional ornament. The clasp, of the same style as the smaller links (B), is a pinch-flange clasp, the socket being decorated with four triangular, rose-cut diamonds, the pinch flange with two.

Length 20⅞ (53)
Width of widest link 1¹³⁄₁₆ (2.1)
Collections
   Duke of Saxe-Coburg-Gotha
   Bensimon, Paris
Exhibited
   Walters Art Gallery (1948)
   Art Institute of Chicago (1951–1962) RX200/5
Published
   D'Otrange (1952) p. 69, ill. p. 72
BMA L.62.15.75
Gutman 612

Mr. Gutman, the Art Institute of Chicago and D'Otrange have all called this necklace "Italian, 16th century," a serviceable attribution if unnecessarily broad in date. Although the eight larger links are neither delicate nor robust enough to indicate any later date than that suggested by them, the seven smaller links, with their asymmetrical design, if not originally part of the assemblage, could be assigned to a somewhat later time. In accepting the general Italian provenance proposed, the cataloguer inclines to the assumption that the larger and smaller links are of different dates and places of origin, on the ground that the style of the former, which are *ajouré*, partake of a massiveness associable with the late 16th century (cf. no. 59), whereas the smaller links, which are closed, are more delicate and suggest parallels in their style with work from the first half of the 17th century.

The seven smaller links with their asymmetrical carriage and technical differences, should be assigned, therefore, to a later time. Were both sets of links from the same workshop, it would have been natural for enameling and punch-tooling to have been carried through consistently, which it is not. The triangular collets of the obverse of these smaller links are more typical of the designers of 1620–1630, Symony and Lemercier especially.

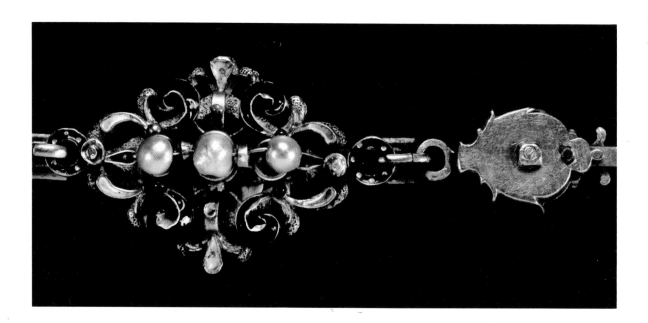

58   Necklace of Eleven Medallions in Gold, Enamel and Diamonds

SOUTH GERMAN   CA. 1600

The necklace is composed of eleven medallions joined by short chains of three plain gold links. The medallions are of three specifically different types. Four medallions are of type A, two at each end of the necklace. A cast and carved openwork frame serves as the support for a square, table-cut, collet-mounted diamond, the wall of which is surrounded by eight opaque white and translucent green enamel three-part leaves forming a rosette. This is attached to the base by a central rivet. Three medallions are of type B (a pair adjacent to type A and one other) and are very similar to type A though brighter in color. The base is enameled translucent red and green, and opaque black and white, and the leaf rosette at the base of the wall of the collet is also enameled translucent red and green, and opaque white. The reverse of type B is enameled opaque black and white. The four remaining medallions are of type C and are the largest and most elaborate. The scrollwork of the base, enameled opaque black and white, and translucent red and green, is of more profuse curvature. The translucent red enamel is of a darker and richer color than type B, but the rosettes and mounts of the central diamonds are identical. One of these medallions (the sixth from the end, and at mid-point in the necklace) is probably a replacement made to match; its gold is much brighter, the enamel—both obverse and reverse, has a slicker surface and the top is finished off by a tiny red pellet. Two additional rings on the inner corners of each medallion indicate either suspension points for further ornament or for some other attachment purpose.

Length omitting ring clasp 11 (28)
Width of largest medallion 5⁄19 (1.5)
Collections
    Luigi Grassi
    Henry Walters
Exhibited
    Walters Art Gallery (1948)
Published
    Grassi Sale (1927) p. 171, no. 457
    Walters Sale (1941) p. 324, no. 1102, ill. p. 325
BMA L.62.15.144
Gutman 951

    This jewel offers very informative details relevant to its original use. The purpose of the medallions now joined as a necklace should be discussed before the question of date and provenance are broached. As now held together—each medallion by three plain gold links attached to the larger pairs of rings on each medallion—the medallions are out of balance. Unless counter-weighted by pendants, they would have turned and twisted into disarray. Since there are no traces of abrasion except in the rings now holding the loops, and none on the back of any medallion, the original use of the medallions may well have been as ornaments sewed to the raiment.

This practice, while not confined to one country, was somewhat less popular in Italy than in Germany, Spain and especially England, and in the period ca. 1570 to ca. 1615, as exemplified by the royal portraits by Sanchez-Coello, the portraits of Elizabeth, and the portrait of Magdalena, Duchess of Neuburg, attributed to Pietro Candido, ca. 1613, in the Bavarian State Collection, Munich. The difference in size, technique and coloration among the medallions would tend to corroborate the conclusion that the units were meant to be sewn on various parts of a gown.

There are few traits sufficiently marked to serve as indices of provenance: one can only comment that the delicate ornateness of the structure resembles German taste more closely than Italian.

59

Necklace of Twelve Medallions in Gold, Enamel and Gems

The necklace consists of twelve *ajouré* links of two specific designs, six links each, and each design with slight internal variations. Design A (from loop end) can be found in links 1, 3, 5, 7, 9 and 11. The base consists of a wax cast *ajouré* frustum of a splayed cone, the open top of which is reinforced by two bars at right angles. The design is a series of symmetrical interlocking scrolls, fleurs-de-lis and tendrils emerging from calices, enameled opaque white, black, blue and green, and translucent green, blue-green, and a frosty opaque white. The unenameled surfaces have been given a mat finish with two kinds of punch-tooling—single convex point punch, and a hollow cylindrical punch. Centering each cone is a high, rectangular pyramidal collet composed of an ovolo plinth supporting a tapering pedestal, the four edges of which curve upward half-way on each side to form a double scallop. The pedestal supports either a step-cut diamond, links (from upper left) 1, 7 and 9, or a table-cut ruby, links 3, 5 and 11. The enameling of the diamond mounts is opaque black and blue with identical patterns in links 1 and 7 and of variant patterns in link 9, and for the rubies, opaque black and white with identical patterns in each of the three. The *ajouré* cone base of link 9 is further exceptional in that here the frosty white enamel of the scrolls, to left and right of the collet, is replaced by dark translucent red. Design B can be found in links 2, 4, 6, 8, 10 and 12. Here the base consists also of the wax cast *ajouré* frustum of a splayed cone, but the profile is convex rather than concave. The dimensions are slightly smaller than design A and the effect generally airier. Scrolls, fleurs-de-lis and tendrils are employed with the area of enamel (opaque white, black, blue and green) somewhat reduced. Unenameled surfaces are tooled with both the point punch and the tubular punch. Instead of the collet of design A, the center consists of four separate parts, bolted through the crossbars. Part 1 consists of an X, each end of which terminates in two butterfly wings with translucent blue-green enamel pellets. Part 2 consists of a hollow, square, columnar support from each side of which extend cylindrical arms to form a cross, parallel to the crossbar of the base; each arm terminates in a scalloped canopy and a boss. Part 3 is a smaller X with tapering pointed oval arms. Part 4 is the inverted pyramidal collet of the table-cut ruby. Aside from minute variations within the enamel, each link of design B is identical. The bolt, by means of which these parts are all held together, is a solid square bar which holds the collet of the ruby. Each part has been separately cast and filed to its appropriate finish. The crossbars of design A are cast as part of the *ajouré* design of the base. The crossbars of design B, being of somewhat slimmer dimensions, have been fused into the basic design. Each link of design A has two cast loops to right and left through which two tongues, soldered to the underside of the base of the links of design B, are bent. The final link of design B hooks through the first link of design A.

Length 17 (43)
Collection
   Duke of Saxe-Coburg-Gotha
Exhibited
   California Palace of the Legion of Honor (1942)
Published
   California Palace (1942) p. 30, no. 207. ill.
BMA L.62.15.246
Gutman 1224

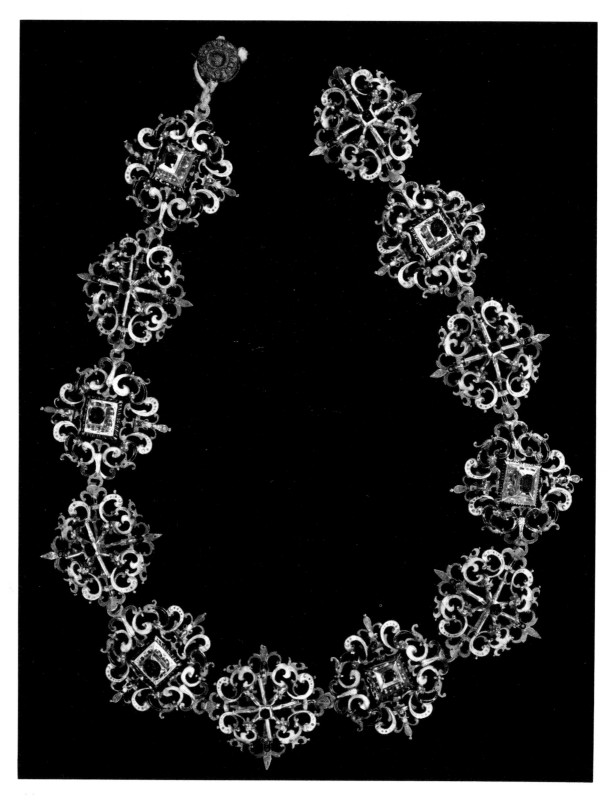

Though probably much diminished in the number of links, this necklace is not only of super-fine workmanship but, because of the technical identities between the two types of units, unexceptionable as an ensemble. Microscopic examination reveals that the punch-tooling of all surfaces so finished was effected by the same implements; there is also no variation in the quality or color of the enamel.

Both vendor and collector attribute the piece to Hans Mielich. In the cataloguer's opinion this attribution must be examined. Our primary evidence of Mielich's highly personal style, the miniatures on parchment of the *Kleinodienschatz* of Albert V, Duke of Bavaria, now in the Bayerisches Nationalmuseum, Munich, show him as a late-Renaissance artist engaged in the compacting of abstract, natural and architectural motifs into what are in truth decorative hodgepodges. Each element is so clotted with the designer's vocabulary that no distinct or explicit statement is made. Each is incapable, quite literally, of being seen through: the backs of the designs are just as grumous and impenetrable as the fronts. The necklace here possesses a wholly different character.

The mounts in the center of each link of design A at first signify a South German provenance, although it is admissable that the prominence given the fleurs-de-lis, and the manner in which, in the links of design B, unenameled flat gold hooks appear at four corners—so reminiscent of early 17th century engraved designs—forces one to consider the possibility of French origin. So little of French jewelry has survived that an exact parallel cannot be cited.

But a comparison with no. 31, a pendant assigned to South Germany, is instructive. While both are ultimately indebted to the same engravers' designs, the pendant displays just that same proneness to attractive intemperance and immoderation that truly marks the designs of Hans Mielich. Whereas the necklace is unmistakably structural, with every component distinct, the pendant tends to be blurred and uncertain, supersaturated with visual richness.

One further comparison would seem to confirm a southern and Germanic origin, for there is in the Kunsthistorische Museum at Vienna a necklace containing links identical in style, and coming from the convent in Hall, Tirol, Austria (Kertesz [1947] p. 415, ill. at bottom of page) assigned by Kertesz to the transitional movements between the Late Renaissance and the Baroque (*ibid.*, pp. 416–417).

It is also possible that the components of the necklace were once used not to form a necklace but as sewn-on dress ornaments, as shown in a portrait of Princess Mary of Orange, about 1600 (Gans [1961] fig. 27).

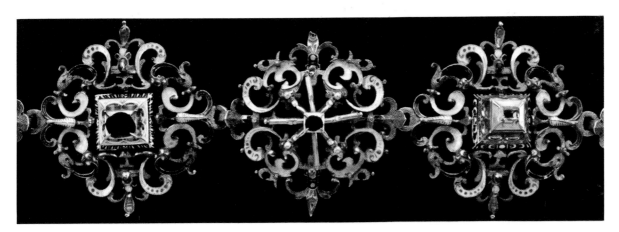

60   Pair of Bracelets in Gold and Enamel

Color plate opposite

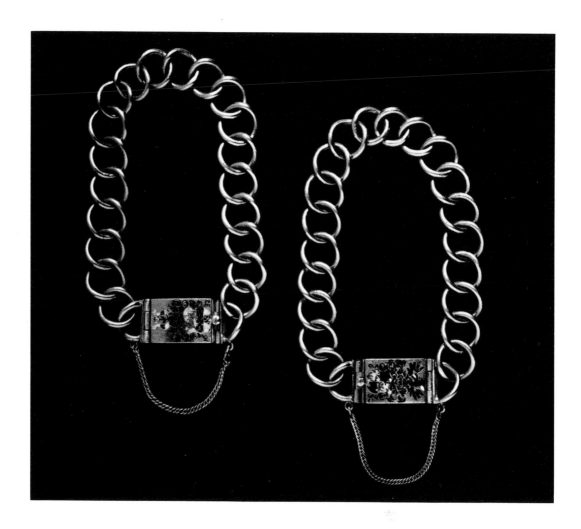

The bracelets are composed of twenty heavy, plain links and two half-links, one on each clasp. The housing of the spade-flange clasp on each bracelet bears an unidentified coat-of-arms in *champlevé* enamel in opaque white and black, and translucent green, blue, orange and red. On each, divided by the bottom part of the shield, the date 1632. The two sections of each clasp are connected by a fine gold chain.

60

64

30

47

Height of one bracelet 3 ⅞₆ (8.8)
Height of the other 3 ½ (8.9)
Width at clasp 1 ½ (3.8)
Collection
    Marc Rosenberg
Exhibited
    Art Institute of Chicago (1951–1962) RX 200/53
Published
    Rosenberg Sale (1929) p. 46 no. 236a, ill. pl. 23
    D'Otrange (1952) p. 72
BMA L.62.15.121
Gutman 1051

According to the Rosenberg Sale catalogue (1929) the bracelets were labeled "Saxon" and said to have been found in a grave. Save for a normal amount of loss in the enamel, they are of undiminished brilliance. Clifford Smith (1909, p. 226, pl. XXXVII, XI) cites a similar one of two in the Victoria and Albert Museum, and mentions that three similar bracelets form part of the Holtzendorf treasure from Pinnow in Brandenburg in the Germanic Museum, Nürnberg. These also have flat clasps and coat-of-arms; one is dated 1612. The most striking parallel is found in a pair of bracelets worn by a woman in a portrait by Michael Conrad Hirt (ca. 1615–ca. 1695) in the Dayton Art Institute, Dayton, Ohio (acc. no. 5571). Worn on either wrist, the enameled crests, though too cursory in the brush-work to be identified, are contained within identical rectangular units; the links of the chains, however, are complected, rather than open as in the Gutman example.

Dr. Klemens Stadler, Director of Bavarian Archives, whose help has been sought in a vain effort to identify the devices, has suggested they they could indeed be German, and proposed possible new avenues of research, which will be pursued. In the meantime the heraldry remains unidentified.

170

61   Crown for a Religious Figure in Gold, Enamel, Emeralds and Diamonds

SPANISH COLONIAL   EARLY 17TH CENTURY

This elaborate and costly object is made of a number of separate parts, of which the fastening together is an essential part of the description. The basic structure of the entirety is of massy gold, cast and carved for the reception of external enamel and, on the interior, filed (but not polished) to present a kind of mat brocaded effect; some exterior details have been highly burnished. Part 1, at the summit, is a cross *Avellan* of translucent green enamel. The two arms and the head of the cross end in four-petal flowers of translucent yellow enamel, with opaque white enamel centers. Part 2 is the four-handled finial enameled opaque white and blue, and translucent green and yellow. Part 3, the base of the finial, consists of a beak-and-scotia molding enameled in bands of translucent green and yellow. Part 4 is a square plate of burnished gold, with corners terminating in fleurs-de-lis, enameled translucent green and yellow. This square plate serves as the bed for Parts 1, 2 and 3 above, which are held together by a bolt running through the core, the termination of which is a pendant cabochon emerald. Part 4 also serves as the fastening for Parts 5, 6, 7 and 8. These consist of identical curved openwork plaques of scrolls, volutes, fleurs-de-lis and florettes, enameled opaque white, blue and black, and translucent yellow and green. Each of the plaques is provided at bottom and top with a rectangular flange which, at the top, fits into a groove in the bottom of Part 4, where it is bolted. In the center of the upper surface of each top flange of Parts 5, 6, 7 and 8 is a small depression, with indications of the presence of opaque white enamel, and perhaps an additional gem. Each rectangular flange is bolted to Part 9 (described below). In the center of each plaque is a square, table-cut emerald in a collet mount which forms the center of a separate enameled cartouche of two fleurs-de-lis, enameled opaque white and black. The cartouche is fastened through the plaque by two cotter-pins, top and bottom. To the left and right are smaller square, table-cut emeralds in collet mounts, forming the center of eight-petal florettes enameled black and white, which are fastened through the plaque by single cotter-pins. Above and below the center cartouche are larger square, table-cut emeralds in collet mounts, also forming the centers of square florettes enameled black and white, riveted through the plaque. This decoration is consistent on each plaque save one, in which the left-hand small table-cut emerald is missing. Here the collet contains some soft black material, originally used as an adhesive. Part 9 consists of the lower section of the crown, a coronal of eight points, four major and four minor. The major points are triangular, open-work compositions of scrolls and volutes ending in fleur-de-lis finials. The enamel is consistent with Parts 5, 6, 7 and 8, being opaque blue and white, and translucent green and yellow. The center of each major point consists of an opaque black and white enameled device with, at the bottom, a large collet-mounted emerald of varying shape and cut. Above, with large emeralds, are smaller stones (diamonds, emerald and aquamarine) also of varying shape and cut. These four devices are fastened through the four major points by two cotter-pins, top and bottom. The four minor points consist also of the same triangular compositions, but are shorter and more compact, and do not have the fleur-de-lis finial. In the center of each of these is an opaque white and black enameled device centered by a single large table-cut emerald, fastened through the back by smaller cotter-pins. Part 10, the circular base of the crown, consists of two torus moldings with a flat channel between. This channel contains Part 11, a semi-circular band of nineteen square, table-cut

171

diamonds, collet-mounted, in reddish gold, and Part 12, a semi-circular band of twenty-one table-cut emeralds, collet-mounted, also in reddish gold. Each of the bands is fastened in the channel of Part 10 by a single split rivet. Part 13 consists of a flat band soldered on the interior of Part 10, with a circular hole for the attachment of the crown to the head of the image.

Height 5⁵⁄₁₆ (13.5)
Diameter at largest point 3⁹⁄₁₆ (9.1)
BMA L.63.2.240
Gutman 1384

The technique and visual effect are absolutely consistent, and curiously sophisticated and primitive at the same time. The translucent enamel, both green and yellow, is marked by numerous bubbles, indicating either over-firing or imperfectly mixed frit. On the other hand, the opaque enamel has a hard, vitreous finish. The opaque blue is consistently mottled with small white flecks. The exterior carving (consisting largely of flutes on the unenameled portions) is regular and precise. The collets are smooth, tight and even. The interior surface of the crown, however, has preserved a rougher finish in which both rivets and cotter-pins play a distinct aesthetic role: the contrast between external gloss and internal glow, punctuated by the gems and their somewhat rugged fastenings, effects a counterpoint that adds both to the crown's three-dimensionality and its sumptuousness. It is to be noted that the head of every bolt is carefully shaped to a kind of Maltese Cross with notched points and curved sides. With the exception of the missing emerald noted above, and a few abrasions in the enamel, the object is in superb condition.

A certificate in the possession of the collector, signed by Mr. Luis E. Varcarcel, Director of the National Museum of Lima, Peru, dated August 21, 1933, speaks of the piece as "una joya valiosa de la orfebrería peruana colonial, con una untigüedad de no menos de tres siglos." This would put the work in the early 17th century.

62 Oval Pendant Locket in Gold and Enamel: Portrait Miniature of Molière

FRENCH   CA. 1620 AND 1660

The body of the locket is suspended from a gold ring with downward turning volutes forming a truncated trefoil, which is soldered to the wall of the locket. Both faces consist of an identical pattern of scrolls, leaves and clustered dots around a central twelve-petaled rosette, all originally in *email en resille sur verre* with a translucent dark green ground. The greater part of the enamel is missing, leaving only the gold foil bed, which has become detached in places from the glass channels. The remaining enamel indicates a color scheme of opaque white, yellow, light green and dark blue, and translucent red and green. The front has a diagonal crack (which is apparently only superficial) in the glass ground running from left to right. The upper portion of the back has a similar diagonal crack from right to left which is deeper and has resulted in the partial sheering away and fracture of the glass. The exterior wall is an unornamented gold band edged with two plain convex mouldings. The front face is secured by a simple peg catch and, moving on a pin hinge, opens from below to disclose the miniature. This is a fine bright portrait bust of Molière, looking three-quarters right, in open-neck shirt and red surcoat, crowned with a profuse laurel wreath tied in front with a red bow. The inside surface of the lid bears the engraved legend, filled with hard black wax or bitumen:
DONNÉ À/Mme LA COMTESSE/DE FEUQUIERES/PAR SON AMI/MOLIERE/MDCLX

Height including loop 1 7/16 (3.6)
Width 1 (2.6)
Collections
    Seymour
    E. Peter Jones
Publications
    Jones Sale (1958) no. 75, ill.
BMA L.62.15.70
Gutman 1354

The locket case is a typical example of a small group of objects in this exceptional and chronologically limited technique (for discussion see no. 45). In design it is so close to another in the Victoria and Albert Museum (M. 65–1952, given by Dr. Joan Evans, dated in the Register, 1952, as "about 1620") (Evans [1953] pl. VII (a), "French, ca. 1610") that both must have come not only from the same designer but from the same workshop.

The miniature and interior inscription present questions less easily answered. The portrait—a strongly idealized likeness—would appear to have been done about the same time as that of Molière as Julius Caesar, attributed to Pierre Mignard, his life-long friend, in the Comédie Française, undated, of which it was said the sitter was *plein de lauriers comme un jambon de Mayence*.

174

It is not easy to connect Molière, the date of the inscription, and any of the family Manassès de Pas, Marquises de Feuquières. Molière, it is true, was patronized during his provincial career by the Duc d'Epernon; from 1653 he was on more convivial terms with the Prince de Conti. He was certainly not poor (in February 1656, he received from the treasury of the Estates 6,000 *livres*) so he could, indeed, have afforded the purchase of even so rare a bit of *bijouterie* as the locket in *email en resille sur verre*. By the end of 1658 he had already appeared before the king and his court (in the *Nicomède* of Corneille) under the protection of the Duc d'Orleans. In Paris, between December 2, 1659 and Easter, 1660, thirty-two performances of *Les Précieuses Ridicules* had been given, ending with a royal performance in the autumn and a grant of 3,000 *livres*. He was, therefore, in a contact with the court as intimate as the deteriorating protocol of the epoch would permit.

Pierre Mignard, the painter, married Anna Avolara in 1660. Their daughter, Catharine-Marguerite Mignard, was born in Rome in 1657 and married, October 1, 1696, Jules Pas, Comte de Feuquières (died 1741), one of the seven sons of Isaac Manassès de Pas, Marquis de Feuquières (1618–1688) and Anne-Louise de Granemont. Thus it is only in 1696 that, through Mignard, Molière can be brought into a dated connection with a "Comtesse de Feuquières." No mention of Molière as a friend of the de Pas family is made in the "Lettres inédites des Feuquières" of August Alphonse Étienne-Gallois (Paris, 1845, five volumes) the best source of information. In Volume II, however, the letters skip from May 17, 1659 to April 3, 1665.

There is no good ground to suspect the inscription as a fictitious interpolation, yet as a document the portrait and inscription would add materially to the data of *molièrisme* were a demonstrable connection to be ascertained.

63 Pendant Locket of Painted Enamel with Signed Miniature by Alexander Cooper

DUTCH   CA. 1632

The locket consists of an ellipse with hinged snap catch, enameled on the front, back and sides with painted flowers on an opaque white ground. The colors are primarily blue, yellow, orange, green, violet, pink and black. The sides have been chipped and filled with dull opaque white enamel. The miniature is a portrait of a man, three-quarter profile to left, on a dark blue ground. Fine curly brown hair falls to the shoulders; his mustache and goatee are yellowish, and his eyes are blue. A wide, white collar with lace border falls on a buttoned black doublet. In the lower left, in brown on the blue ground, in Roman letters, the initials AC.

Height from stationary loop 2³⁄₁₆ (5.6)
Width 1¹¹⁄₁₆ (4.2)
Collections
    J. Pierpont Morgan
    Robert H. Rockliff, Esq.
Exhibited
    Art Institute of Chicago (1951–1962) RX200/40
Published
    Morgan Sale (1935) p. 14, no. 21
    Rockliff Sale (1947) no. 748, ill. pl. 2
BMA L.62.15.109
Gutman 1001

Both Mr. Gutman and the Art Institute of Chicago have assigned the locket to Germany, Nürnberg (?), 17th century, on the basis of comparisons with the work of Johann Heel (cf. Honey [1932] pp. 132–140, and [1935] pp. 266–271).

While there is a resemblance between Heel's work and the painting of the locket, both chronologically and stylistically a Dutch provenance of between 1630 and 1635 can better be sustained. First, the decoration of the locket itself is in the vein of the botanical illustrations prevalent and accessible between de Bry's *Florilegium Novum* of 1612, N. Cochin's *Livre nouveau de fleurs* of 1635 and François Lefebre's *Livre de fleurs* of 1639. Joan Evans (1931, I, pp. 78 ff.) has traced the growth of floriculture and its decorative consequences from the foundation of the Jardin du Roi (later the Jardin des Plantes) in the reign of Henry IV to Grinling Gibbons. It is to be noted that the first spate of publications with naturalistic botanical

176

specimens falls between Paul Flindt in 1593 and Langlois' engravings of 1648. This would effectively rule out Johann Heel, born in Augsburg, October 25, 1637, and died in Nürnberg, March 17, 1709.

The tulip, so prominently featured on both sides of the locket, was first brought to Vienna in 1554 by Ogier Ghiselin de Busbecq, Ambassador of Ferdinand I to Suleiman the Magnificent. The Fuggers of Augsburg, in 1561, commissioned Konrad Gessner to bring tulip bulbs from the Levant: the first printed picture occurs in Gessner's *De Hortis Germaniae*, Basle, 1561. The first bulbs reached Antwerp in 1561, and, cultivated especially in the vicinity of Haarlem, became, in 1636 and 1637, the objects of tulipomania and unbridled financial speculation. Rarer bulbs fetched enormous prices: a "Semper Augustus" was sold for 13,000 florins and an "Admiral Liefkens" for 4,500 florins; a speculator in Amsterdam profited 68,000 florins in four months. By 1638, the craze was completely deflated, and a "Semper Augustus" could be had for 50 florins.

It is precisely between January 1632 and October 1633 that Alexander Cooper (1605?–1660) can be traced to The Hague. Since the miniature is traditionally assumed to be Prince Maurice, son of King Frederick V of Bohemia (died 1632) this would connect it with Cooper's only dated work, the medallion chain with twelve oval portraits of that monarch, his wife Elizabeth, and their children, in the former Kaiser-Friedrich Museum, Berlin.

The combination of circumstances enables us to assume, with good reason, that the locket and miniature are of the same date and origin, that is, Dutch, between 1632 and 1633.

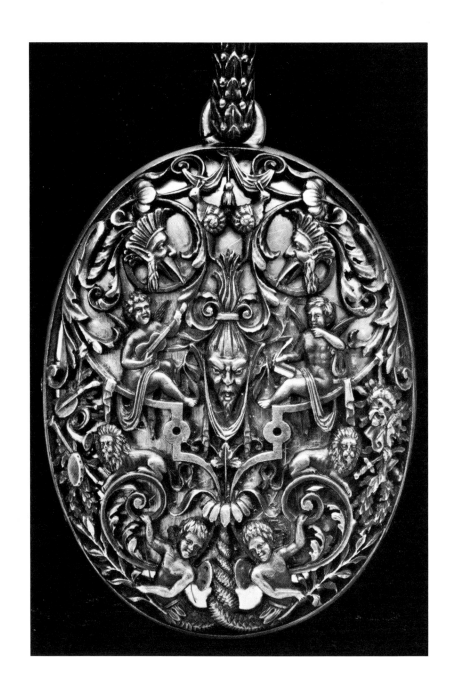

178

64   Pendant Locket of *Ajouré* Steel over Gold

GERMAN   LATE 16TH CENTURY   *Color plate facing page 168*

The elliptical, gold hinged case is covered, obverse and reverse, by an *ajouré* second casing of cast and chased steel. The obverse (a hinged lid, opening left to right) presents an intricate design of foliations, scrolls, drapery, swags and ribbons, with two cupids, the left one with palette and maulstick painting before an easel, to right a cupid with hammer in upraised right hand and chisel in left carving a figure. The lower limbs of these two figures twist into conical coils. Between the cupids, a female mascaron, full face, with elaborate scrolled and scalloped headdress; seated upon, or interwoven with, the foliage, two rabbits, two birds and two serpents. The reverse presents, on either side of a very much elongated, bearded mascaron with hair clasped in a topknot, between two volutes, to left a seated cupid playing a guitar, to right a seated cupid writing music, pen in right hand, his left elbow resting on a lyre. Again interwoven with or resting on the foliations and garlands, two snails, two profile mascarons, two couchant lions and two mer-cupids with tails intertwined into a conical coil. There are numerous musical instruments including a *tromba marina* (?), tambourine, hunting horn and lute. The locket is suspended from a gold-lined, steel, laurel-wreath ring. The interior is plain reddish gold.

Height from stationary loop 1⅝ (4.2)
Width 1³⁄₁₆ (3)
BMA L.62.15.169
Gutman 1417

Of all the pieces in the collection this, in its fashion, offers the most striking problems in connoisseurship and stylistic analysis. The collector assigns it to Nürnberg or Augsburg, between 1540 and 1560. This would appear to be several decades too early. The closest decorative affinities are to be found in the work of Theodore de Bry (1528–1598) who worked in Frankfurt am Main between 1570 and 1598, with the exception of three years spent in England, 1586–1589. Plates of ornaments produced by de Bry (Hollstein, IV, pp. 48 and 50, with illustrations) contain almost all the elements here combined. An engraved pocket watch formerly in the Eugen Gutman collection (von Falke [1912] no. 285, pl. 68) of gilt bronze, called German, 17th century, though with fewer figures and more luxuriant foliage, continues this tradition. A watch case of pierced and engraved silver by Klotz of Augsburg, of the end of the 16th century (Evans [1953] pl. 98a) and another of pierced and enameled gold in the style of Daniel Mignot (*ibid.*, pl. 98b) the first in the Fitzwilliam Museum, the second in the Victoria and Albert Museum, attest that this technique was common to the period presumed. The style epitomized in this piece came to be much admired and was imitated by late 19th century French goldsmiths.

179

65

Gold Comfit Box in the Form of a Book

NORTH GERMANY   1621

The box is in the form of a book which opens on a four-part hinge. The front bears a polygram and the date 1621, incised and filled with bitumen; a circular collet, much damaged, lacks the original stone. The back has an incised square with four double fleurs-de-lis in the corners, four small eight-pointed stars and a six-pointed star in the center; all these are also bitumen filled. A hollow suspension ring is soldered to a hollow, equatored ovoid, in turn soldered to the back half of the "pages." Open, each half is divided by soldered flanges into four square compartments. A hinged tablet, divided on each face into four corresponding squares, is engraved with the intended contents of each compartment beneath. These are:

SLAG .B.—one or more of the ingredients for "Schlagwasser," *Aqua apoplectica*, a cardiac stimulant made of brandy, primrose petals and violets (cf. Johann Theodor Jablonskies, "Allgemeines Lexicon der Kuenste und Wissenschaften," Königsberg and Leipzig, 1767, p. 1296, col. 1).
MVSCATEN .B.—nutmeg
CIMT .B.—cinnamon
ROSEN .B.—rose petals
NEGELKEN .B.—cloves
ANNIS .B.—anise
ZANEN .SA.—teeth. The powdered tooth root of both humans and animals was used as a medicament for a preposterous variety of ailments and illnesses, from impotence to tetanus.

The box is held shut by a pin bolt at the end of a plain, linked gold chain.

Height including suspension ring 1¹⁵⁄₁₆ (5)
Height without suspension ring 1 ³⁄₁₆ (3)
Width 1 (2.5)
Depth ⁷⁄₁₆ (1.2)
BMA L.62.15.188
Gutman unnumbered

The polygram, which has not been deciphered, consists of a superimposed M, W and S. The serifs of the left and right arms of the W form a G and a B respectively, while those of the M form a D (P?) and an L. The curves of the S, crossing both M and W, could provide a number of A's, but it seems more probable that we have interlaced consonants representing the initials of two lovers.

66 Silver Gilt Comfit Box in the Form of a Skull

GERMAN   17TH CENTURY

The skull is cast and carved and opens from the top on a five-part pin hinge along the coronal suture. In the front half the eye sockets, nasal openings and teeth are pierced through; a pierced screen above the upper row of teeth permits additional ventilation. Inside the two halves are separated by a hinged tablet engraved in front with a pattern of leaves, in back with labels for the four adjacent compartments: SCHLAG (ingredients for *Schlagwasser*, see no. 65), CANEL (cinnamon), MUSCHA (nutmeg), NEGEL (cloves). The back half of the skull contains four compartments of equal size with soldered walls. At the back and base of the skull are two crossed bones. The halves are held together by a fastening constructed of an internal spring band depressed by a button on top of the front half. There are no hallmarks.

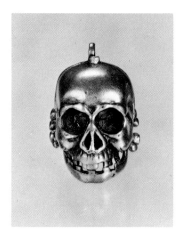 

Height 1 ¹⁄₁₆ (2.6)
Diameter from front
   to back 1 ¹⁄₁₆ (2.6)
Diameter from side to
   side ¹³⁄₁₆ (2.1)
BMA L.63.2.236
Gutman unnumbered

A nearly identical piece is in the Croft-Lyons Bequest of the Victoria and Albert Museum (no. M.804–1926), a German "scent bottle or perfume case" of the 17th century.

The use of a human skull for spices and comfits is really no more unsuitable or macabre than a marriage solemnized at Forest Lawn. Germany of the Thirty Years War (1618–1648), a cockpit of contending religious mercenaries then and for several generations thereafter, was so devastated that the *memento mori* was as much a part of the daily scene then as the phrase "live it up!" is today. The skull, as an adjunct of the Reformation, appears notably in Holbein's *Ambassadors* of 1533, perhaps as the personal device of Jean de Dinteville; but by the 17th century the vanity of human existence and its end in corruption had become obsessive and (by way of a parallel) is a favored subject of Dutch painters. Likewise, pendants of skulls, coffins and skulls-and-crossbones, with hortatory inscriptions (Steingräber [1956] figs. 259–261) occur, and figures of Death as a carrion-festooned skeleton are carved (cf., the two lindenwood Upper Rhenish figures in the Busch-Reisinger Museum, Harvard University, Kuhn [1965] nos. 54 and 55). Johann Georg Hainz, the Hamburg painter, included a skull among the objects of his "Jewel Cupboard" (1666) now in the Hamburg Kunsthalle.

67 Silver Pomander

SPANISH OR SPANISH COLONIAL   LATE 16TH CENTURY

The eight segments are held in place by a domed screw cap surmounted by a finial with a bird, inserted in the hollow, octagonal column of the center. Each of the eight segments is engraved on the exterior with a design of four scrolls filled with horizontal lines. The sliding covers and the octagonal column on the interior bear a design of concentric square and diagonal lines. The cover is missing from one segment. Beneath the finial the cap is engraved with an eight-leaved rosette. There are no hallmarks.

Height 2¼ (5.7)
Width 1¾ (4.4)
BMA L.62.15.212
Gutman 1310

In the absence of hallmarks and labels upon the covers of the compartments, as well as a lack of clear stylistic clues, assignment of date and provenance to this piece are problematical. Mr. Gutman considers it Spanish of the late 16th century. The cataloguer is inclined to agree, with the proviso that the date may be later and the "Spanish" designation should perhaps be enlarged to include Colonial work, Peruvian or Argentinean, although it must be observed that 16th century Spanish works in The Hispanic Society of America (Johnson [1944] pp. 184–185, 190–191, 192, 194–195 [the scrolls of the spout especially] 198 and 200) which display analogous decoration and design are more severe in proportions, and finials, when they occur, are strictly architectural or geometric. The 17th century sweetmeat box (*ibid.*, p. 232) and the 18th century Argentinean *maté* cup with the cock on the handle (*ibid.*, p. 266) (the bird's tail in the Gutman piece has evidently been broken off) have the ampler proportions of the Baroque.

68 Pomander in Silver Gilt and Enamel

DUTCH   17TH CENTURY

The pomander, pear-shaped when closed, is suspended by a foliated ring from a hemispherical screw cap, decorated with semi-circular scales, which screws down over the tips of the segments to hold them in place. Four segments fall back on simple pin-hinges from a central square interior column. Each segment on the outside has a convex oval enamel plaque painted with a design of a stemmed *coupe* filled with fruit, leaves and flowers. The colors are yellow, orange, blue, green and black on opaque white. Surrounding each plaque is a cast and punch-tooled design of flowers and scrolls. On the interior, each segment has a double compartment closed by a sliding cover. On the inside of two of these covers are engraved respectively VIII I and VIII III. The inside right bottom corner of each segment also contains the numeral VIII. The pomander terminates in an eight-leaved rosette.

Height 1⅞ (4.8)
Diameter ⅞ (2.2)
Collection
   Earl of Harewood
BMA L.62.15.210
Gutman 1303 G

The Victoria and Albert Museum possesses an example (no. 221–1865) of painted enamel on copper, Dutch, 17th century (though referred to in the Inventory of Art Objects, 1865, p. 25, as "on gold, French, about 1620"). The painted enamel flowers are not markedly different in either technique or representation from those in no. 63 in this catalogue, though less dispersed.

184

69   Six-Part Pomander in Gold, Enamel and Gems

FRENCH   EARLY 17TH CENTURY   *Color plate facing page 186*

This piece is so elaborate that the description must necessarily be somewhat abbreviated. Closed, the vessel consists of a melon-shaped, six-part center container, the segments of which are held in place by the usual screw cap, in this case a *coupe* filled from above with three rectangular table-cut diamonds in collet mounts and three strapwork scrolls enameled translucent red which surround the baluster ring enameled opaque white, black and blue. The broad flare of the base of the cap, which holds in place the top ends of the segments, is decorated with opaque white and black arabesques on a gouge-carved ground. Each segment is bordered with a torus containing a spiral of opaque white and black enamel. This frames a *champlevé* enamel field—so fine as to seem to be cloisonné—of two different designs, each design applied alternately to the six segments. This consists of an interlacing of leaves, tendrils and blossoms enameled opaque white, yellow, black and light green, and translucent red, green, yellow and dark blue on a deep blue-green ground. In the center of each panel is a raised, cast and carved cartouche bolted to the surface, enameled opaque white, blue and black, and translucent red; the center of three cartouches containing each a table-cut, collet-mounted diamond, and three a table-cut, collet-mounted ruby. Each segment is separately hinged at the bottom. The base has four panels continuing the *champlevé* enamel decoration of the segments and a scotia with opaque black and white arabesques between which are set six alternating table-cut, collet-mounted diamonds and rubies. Open, the segments reveal a hexagonal supporting column with faces alternately decorated with a *champlevé* enamel pattern of strapwork, cartouches and arabesques in opaque black and white, centering either upon a translucent green oval with quatrefoil rosettes or a translucent red quatrefoil within a hexagon. The sides of each segment are again filled with translucent and opaque *champlevé* enamel fields of the same coloration, alternating three and three between a scheme dominated by two addorsed dolphins on either side of a *tazza* or a floral spray held together in the center by an opaque white enamel torus band. Each compartment is closed by a sliding cover, the handle of which fits into a circular hold at the top of the column. These covers are engraved with the names of six spices:

MVSQ, GIROFLE, MYRRHE, AMBRE, BENIOVIN, CANELLE

Height 4¼ (10.8)
Diameter 2½ (6.4)
Collection
  Henry Walters
Exhibited
  Walters Art Gallery (1948)
Published
  Walters Sale (1943) p. 189
  Hackenbroch (1954), pp. 168–172, ill. pl. 96
BMA L.62.15.220
Gutman 714

An object of such lustrous pomp and faultless entirety as this pomander must necessarily be viewed with both a maximum of gratitude and a maximum of caution. Its existence alone is sufficient to serve as a radical from which important conclusions respecting style and technique may proceed if the requisite facts can be, within reason, ascertained.

Persevering search has failed to disclose ownership before the appearance of the work in the collection of Henry Walters, save that it was acquired from Arnold Seligmann, Rey & Co. Dr. Yvonne Hackenbroch (1954, pp. 168–172, and pl. 96) has published the pomander as German, mid-sixteenth century, "in the style of Holbein the Younger." What connection there is between Holbein's designs and the decorative configuration of the object, or why a German production should have been labeled in French, are unelucidated matters.

The assumption must be made at the outset that the French words for musk, gilly-flowers, myrrh, ambergris, benzoin and cinnamon are prima facie evidence of French origin. The only other problems are to establish a date, and, if possible, a municipal location or atelier.

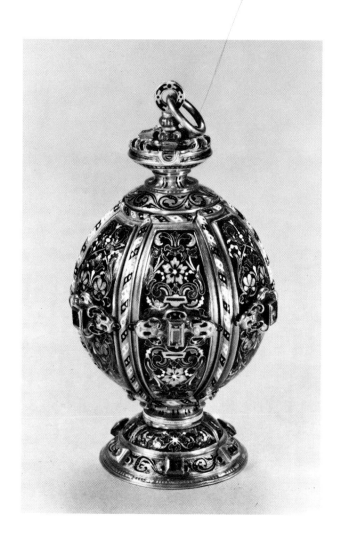

69

The exterior enamel panels of the six segments occupy a place between the somewhat simpler designs of the extant works in *email en resille sur verre* (cf. no. 45) of ca. 1610–1625 and the slenderer grace of the designs of Jacques Hurter and Michel le Blon. The elliptical enamel insert of a reliquary pendant in the Rijksmuseum, Amsterdam (Steingräber [1956] p. 125, fig. 211) given to France with a (?) by this authority, comes as close to the Gutman pomander as any single work. The panels on the interior segments, with their symmetrical foliations girdled by a torus ring, or springing from a squat vessel, are very close to the silhouette designs of M. Christollien's "Petits Panneaud Carrés," undated but published at the beginning of the 17th century (Guilmard [1880] II, no. 22). An architectural, but still indicative parallel, typical of the stylistic tendency during the reign of Louis XIII (1610–1643) to enclose active conventionalized floral motifs in severe, definitive borders, occurs in a chimney piece of the Palace of Fontainebleau of about 1620 (Evans [1931] II, fig. 303).

70   Pendant Perfumer or Sachet

ENGLISH   17TH CENTURY

The container is a hexahedron, each face of which is a quatrefoil cabochon crystal with concave interior. It is suspended by three chains from a splayed tripod composed of three interlocked dolphins, the downward-turning heads of which hold the rings from which the links depend. Each tail supports a pearl with a pin-fastened, eight-lobed collar. Another pearl is suspended from a ring in the center. The bodies of the dolphins are enameled translucent green, with eyes of opaque black. The three upper quatrefoils of the hexahedron are hinged and each opens outward revealing a gold edging into which fits a corresponding gold lip on the hinged cover. Each joint between the quatrefoils on this hexahedron is masked by the bodies of twisted serpents, enameled translucent green, the heads of which bend down over the lower three faces and act as cusps. The tails of the six upper serpents (two for each of the upper three edges) coil over to support a large oval pearl which is topped by an eight-lobed gold collar and an opaque white enamel seagull. Three more birds with folded wings are attached to the top lobe of the three top faces and nestle back against the pearl, acting as both clasps and handles. The lower three faces are fixed and surrounded on their edges by the same coiled serpents, from the heads of four of which depend pin-fastened pearls. The remaining heads and tails are knotted at the bottom.

Height excluding upper suspension ring 3⅜ (8.7)
Width 1 (2.5)
BMA L.63.6.231
Gutman unnumbered

188

This handsome piece is no less puzzling than it is complex in design and construction, nor is the perplexity of the cataloguer alleviated by any clear picture regarding the purpose for which it was originally made. A companion piece in The Metropolitan Museum of Art, New York, while not identical, is so nearly so that it suggests a "pendant pair theory," which might be satisfied by proposing that they once constituted a pair of earrings craftily calculated to disseminate attractive scents around the wearer who would in such instances have been a statuesque person indeed, considering their weight and present length.

It would, for this reason alone, be more defensible to propose a use such as a pendant perfumer to be attached to a dress (cf., Gans [1961] pls. 16, 18, 26, 29 and 117) or even as part of some ornate vanity or dressing table of yet unidentified type.

Miss Yvonne Hackenbroch of The Metropolitan Museum of Art staff reports that their jewel came from the J. P. Morgan Collection in 1917, and writes, "We know little about it though it has been suggested that the appearance of serpents and of doves may suggest a proverb, 'Wise as serpents and harmless as doves'."

The provenance and date are those suggested by Mr. Gutman, and the cataloguer has no alternative proposals.

Bibliography

Armand (1883)
Alfred Armand, *Les Médailleurs italiens des quinzième et seizième siècles*, Paris, 2 ed., 1883

Arte (1919)
Arte y Decoración en España, Casellas Moncanut Hermanos, Barcelona, Vol. III, 1919

Babelon (1897)
Ernest Charles François Babelon, *Catalogue des camées antiques et modernes de la Bibliothéque Nationale*, Paris, 1897

Bache Sale (1945)
Kende Galleries at Gimbel Brothers, *Art Property . . . of the Estate of the Late Jules S. Bache . . .*, New York, April 19–21, 1945

Bassermann-Jordan (1909)
Ernst Bassermann-Jordan, *Der Schmuck*, Leipzig, 1909

Berwind Sale (1939)
Parke-Bernet Galleries, *Valuable Objects of Art . . . From the Collection Formed by the Late Edward J. Berwind . . .*, New York, November 9–11, 1939

von Biedenfeld (1841)
Ferdinand Freiherrn von Biedenfeld, *Geschichte und Verfassung aller geistlichen und weltlichen . . . Ritterorden*, Weimer, 1841

von Boehn (1929)
Max von Boehn, *Modes and Manners: Ornaments*, London, 1929

Bonnaffé (1891)
Edmond Bonnaffé, "Les Bijoux et les Bagues," *La Collection Spitzer*, Vol. III, Paris, 1891, pp. 127–171

de Boot (1536)
Anselmus Boetius de Boot, *Gemmarum et lapidum historia*, ed., Adrianiis Toll, Lugduni Batavorum, 1536

Brewer (1867)
J. S. Brewer, *Letters and Papers, Foreign and Domestic, of the Reign of Henry the Eighth*, London, 1867, *et. seq.*

Bruel (1908)
F. L. Bruel, "Deux inventaires de bagues, joyaux, pierreries et dorures de la reine Marie de Médicis," in *Archives de l'Art Français*, n.s. II, Paris, 1908

Brummer Sale (1949)
Parke-Bernet Galleries, *The Notable Art Collection Belonging to the Estate of the Late Joseph Brummer*, New York, Part I, April 20, 1949, Part II, May 11, 1949

California Palace (1942)
Vanity Fair, California Palace of the Legion of Honor Exhibition, San Francisco, June 16–July 16, 1942

Cook Sale (1925)
Christie's, *Objets d'art, Collection of Humphrey W. Cook, Esq.*, London, July 7, 1925

Cornell (1925)
Henrik Cornell, *Biblia Pauperum*, Stockholm, 1925

Davillier (1879)
Jean Charles Davillier, *Recherches sur l'orfèvrerie en Espagne au moyen age et a la Renaissance*, Paris, 1879

Davenport (1948)
Millia Davenport, *The Book of Costume*, Vol. I, New York, 1948

Desmoni Sale (1960)
Sotheby and Co., *Catalogue of the well known Collection of Renaissance Jewellery, The Property of Martin J. Desmoni, Esq.*, London, May 17, 1960

Detroit (1958)
Decorative Arts of the Italian Renaissance, 1400–1600, The Detroit Institute of Arts Exhibition, Detroit, November 18, 1958–January 4, 1959

D'Otrange (1952)
M. L. d'Otrange, "A Collection of Renaissance Jewels at the Art Institute of Chicago," *The Connoisseur*, September 1952, pp. 66–74

D'Otrange (1953)
M. L. d'Otrange, "Jewels of the XVth and XVIth Centuries," *The Connoisseur*, November 1953, pp. 126–133

Eichler-Kris (1927)
Fritz Eichler and Ernst Kris, *Die Kameen im Kunsthistorischen Museum*, Wien, 1927

Evans (1915)
Joan Evans, "Old English Pendants," *The Connoisseur*, December 1915, pp. 209–216

Evans (1921)
Joan Evans, *English Jewellery from the Fifth Century A.D. to 1800*, London, 1921

Evans (1931)
Joan Evans, *Pattern, A Study of Ornament in Western Europe from 1180 to 1900*, Oxford, 1931

Evans (1953)
Joan Evans, *A History of Jewellery 1100–1870*, New York, 1953

von Falke (1912)
Otto von Falke, *Die Kunstsammlung Eugen Gutman*, Berlin, 1912

von Falke (1928)
Otto von Falke, *Alte Goldschmiedewerke im Zürcher Kunsthaus*, Zürich, 1928

Fogg (1937)
"The Art of the Renaissance Craftsman," Fogg Art Museum Exhibition, Cambridge, May 1937

Forrer (1905)
Robert Forrer, *Geschichte des Gold-und Silberschmuckes nach Originalen der Strassburger historischen Schmuck-Ausstellung von 1904*, Strassburg, 1905

Fürtwängler (1900)
Adolf Furtwängler, *Die antiken Gemmen*, Berlin, 1900

Galter (1948)
Juan Subías Galter, *El arte popular en España*, Barcelona, 1948

Gans (1961)
M. H. Gans, *Juwelen en Mensen*, Amsterdam, 1961

Goldschmidt-Rothschild (1950)
Parke-Bernet Galleries, *Works of Art and Objets de Vertu from the Estate of the Late Baron Max von Goldschmidt-Rothschild*, Part II, New York, April 13–14, 1950

Grassi Sale (1927)
American Art Association, Inc., *Italian Art, The Collection of Professor Luigi Grassi . . . descriptions by Dr. Giacomo de Nicola . . . Dr. Pietro Toesca*, New York, January 20–22, 1927

Guiffrey (1894)
J. Guiffrey, *Inventaires de Jean Duc de Berry, 1401–1416*, 2 vols., Paris, 1894–1896

Guilmard (1880)
D. Guilmard, *Les Maitres Ornemanistes, Texte*, Vol. I, Paris, 1880

Guilmard (1881)
D. Guilmard, *Les Maitres Ornemanistes, Planches*, Vol. II, Paris, 1881

Habich (1923)
Georg Habich, *Die Medaillen der italienischen Renaissance*, Stuttgart and Berlin, 1923

Hackenbroch (1954)
Yvonne Hackenbroch, "Jewellery," *The Concise Encyclopaedia of Antiques*, London, 1954, pp. 168–172

Hackenbroch (1965)
Yvonne Hackenbroch, "Jewels by Giovanni Battista Scolari," *The Connoisseur*, July 1965, pp. 200–205

Herbert (1836)
W. Herbert, *The History of the Twelve Great Livery Companies of London*, 2 vols., London, 1836

Hill (1920)
George F. Hill, *Medals of the Renaissance*, Oxford, 1920

Hollstein, I
F. W. H. Hollstein, *German Engravings, Etchings and Woodcuts, ca. 1400–1700*, Vol. I, Amsterdam, n.d.

Hollstein, IV
F. W. H. Hollstein, *German Engravings, Etchings and Woodcuts, ca. 1400–1700*, Vol. IV, Amsterdam, n.d.

Hollstein, V
F. W. H. Hollstein, *German Engravings, Etchings and Woodcuts, ca. 1400–1700*, Vol. V, Amsterdam, n.d.

Honey (1932)
W. B. Honey, "Johann Heel of Nuremberg," *Burlington Magazine*, March 1932, pp. 132–140

Honey (1935)
W. B. Honey, "Johann Heel: Some Newly Identified Works," *Burlington Magazine*, June 1935, pp. 266–271

Johnson (1944)
Ada Marshall Johnson, *Hispanic Silverwork*, New York, 1944

Johnson (1962)
Ada Marshall Johnson, "Spanish Jewellery of the Late Renaissance," *The Connoisseur Year Book*, 1962

Jones Sale (1958)
Sotheby and Co., *E. Peter Jones, Esq., Catalogue of Fine English and Continental Portrait Miniatures . . .*, London, July 3, 1958

Kertesz (1947)
M. Wagner de Kertesz, *Historia Universal de las Joyas*, Buenos Aires, 1947

Kimball (1943)
Fiske Kimball, *The Creation of the Rococo*, Philadelphia, 1943

Köszeghy (1936)
Elemér Köszeghy, *Magyarországi ötvösjegyek a középkortól 1867-ig. Merkzeichen der Goldschmiede Ungarns vom Mittelalter bis 1867*, Budapest, 1936

Kris (1929)
Ernst Kris, *Meister und Meisterwerke der Steinschneidekunst in der italienischen Renaissance*, Vol. II, Wien, 1929

Kuhn (1965)
Charles L. Kuhn, *German and Netherlandish Sculpture, 1280–1800, the Harvard Collections*, Cambridge, 1965

Kunz (1915)
George Frederick Kunz, *The Magic of Jewels and Charms*, Philadelphia, 1915

Labarte (1879)
J. Labarte, *Inventaire de Charles V, roi de France*, Paris, 1879

Lawrence-Archer (1887)
J. H. Lawrence-Archer, *The Orders of Chivalry*, London, 1887

Lemoisne (1930)
P.-A. Lemoisne, *Les Xylographies des XIVe et XVe Siècles au Cabinet des Estampes de la Bibliothèque Nationale*, Paris and Brussels, 1930

Madame de X Sale (1912)
Hotel Drouot, *Catalogue des Objets de Vitrine Bijoux en or Émaillé du XVIe Siècle . . . Provenant de la Collection de Madame de X . . .*, Paris, March 21, 1912

Marlborough Gems Sale (1899)
Christie's, *Catalogue of the Marlborough Gems*, June 1899

Montaiglon (1861)
A. de Montaiglon, "Joyaux et pierreries . . . de la reine Jeanne d'Évreux," in *Archives de l'art français*, 2nd sér., Vol. I, Paris, 1861

Morgan Sale (1935)
Christie's, *Catalogue of the Famous Collection of Miniatures of the British and Foreign Schools, the Property of J. Pierpont Morgan, Esq.*, London, June 24, 1935

Nichols (1823)
J. Nichols, *The Progresses and Public Processions of Queen Elizabeth*, Vol. I, London, 1823

Palm (1951)
Edwin Walter Palm, "Renaissance Secular Jewellery in the Cathedral of Ciudad Trujillo," *Burlington Magazine*, October 1951, pp. 317–319

Perrot (1820)
Astride M. Perrot, *Collection Historique des Ordres de Chevalerie . . .*, Paris, 1820

Pulszky, Radisics, Molinier (1884)
Charles Pulszky, Eugene Radisics and Emile Molinier, *Chefs-d'oeuvre d'orfèvrerie ayant figuré à l'Exposition de Budapest*, Budapest, Paris, New York and London, 1884

Rockliff Sale (1947)
Sotheby and Co., *Catalogue of Fine Portrait Miniatures, Enamels and Snuff Boxes, The Property of Robert H. Rockliff, Esq., . . .*, London, November 11, 1947

Rosenberg (1911)
Marc Rosenberg, *Studien über Goldschmiedekunst in der Sammlung Figdor*, Wien, 1911

Rosenberg Sale (1929)
Hermann Ball-Paul Graupe, *Sammlung Marc Rosenberg*, Berlin, November 4, 1929

Ross (1941)
Marvin Ross, "Algunos esmaltes del Siglo XVII," *Archivo Español de Arte*, May 1941, pp. 298–299

Rossi (1954)
Filippo Rossi, *Italian Jeweled Arts*, New York, 1954

Salting (1926)
A Guide to the Salting Collection, Victoria and Albert Museum, London, 1926

Schery (1952)
Robert W. Schery, *Plants for Man*, New York, 1952

Schoonebeek (1697)
Adriaan Schoonebeek, *Historie van alle Ridderlyke en Krygsorders . . .*, Amsterdam, 1697

Smith (1909)
H. Clifford Smith, *Jewellery*, London, 2 ed., 1909

Spitzer Sale (1893)
Chevallier, *Catalogue des Objets d'art et de haute curiosité . . . Collection Frederic Spitzer*, Paris, April 17–June 16, 1893

Stein Sale (1886)
Galerie George Petit, *Catalogue des objets d'art . . . Collection Charles Stein*, Paris, 1886

Steingräber (1956)
Erich Steingräber, *Alter Schmuck: Die Kunst des europäischen Schmuckes*, München, 1956

Stone (1958)
Peter Stone, "Baroque Pearls—I," *Apollo*, December 1958, pp. 194–199

Stone (1959)
Peter Stone, "Baroque Pearls—III," *Apollo*, April 1959, p. 108

Tait (1962)
Hugh Tait, "Historiated Tudor Jewellery," *The Antiquaries Journal*, Vol. XLII, Part II, 1962, pp. 226–246

Thoma and Hege (1955)
Hans Thoma, *Kronen und Kleinodien . . . Aufnahmen von Walter Hege*, Berlin, 1955

Waddesdon Bequest (1902)
Charles Hercules Read, *The Waddesdon Bequest, Catalogue of the Works of Art Bequeathed to the British Museum by Baron Ferdinand Rothschild, M. P.*, London, 1902

Waetzoldt (1950)
Wilhelm Waetzoldt, *Dürer and His Times*, New York, 1950

Walters (1926)
H. B. Walters, *Catalogue of Engraved Gems and Cameos in the British Museum*, London, 1926

Walters Sale (1941)
Parke-Bernet Galleries, *The Mrs. Henry Walters Art Collection*, New York, Vol. I, April 23–26, 1941, Vol. II, April 30–May 3, 1941

Walters Sale (1943)
Parke-Bernet Galleries, *Art Collection of the Late Mrs. Henry Walters*, New York, November 30–December 4, 1943

Weinberger Sale (1929)
Dr. Ernst Kris, *Versteigerung der hinterlassenen Sammlung des Herrn Emil Weinberger*, Wien, 1929

Weinmüller (1962)
Weinmüller Auction House, *Freiwillige Versteigerung aus verschiedenem Besitz Antiquitäten . . . Auktion 80, Katalog 88*, Munich, March 14–15, 1962

Williamson (1910)
G. C. Williamson, *Catalogue of the Collection of Jewels and Precious Works of Art, The Property of J. Pierpont Morgan*, London, 1910